THE YOUTH CLUB
IDEAS BOOK

Other books by Sid G. Hedges

GAMES

INDOOR AND COMMUNITY GAMES
MORE INDOOR AND COMMUNITY
    GAMES
OUTDOOR AND COMMUNITY GAMES
OUTDOOR AND PICNIC GAMES
INDOOR GAMES AND FUN
GAMES FOR SOCIALS
MORE GAMES FOR SOCIALS
GAMES FOR THE NOT-SO-YOUNG

PARTY GAMES AND IDEAS
CLASS PARTY GAMES
GAMES FOR SMALL LAWNS
OPEN-AIR GAMES
OUTDOOR GAMES
GAMES TO PLAY
100 GARDEN GAMES
MODERN PARTY GAMES
INDOOR GAMES FOR ALL

YOUTH INTERESTS

THE YOUTH SING BOOK
YOUTH CLUB GAMES AND CONTESTS
YOUTH CLUB EPILOGUES
YOUTH CLUB TECHNIQUE
CLUB ENTERTAINMENT STUNTS
BIBLE CONTEST QUIZZES
SCHOOL ENTERTAINMENT BOOKS
JUNIOR CLUB WORK
CLUB GAMES FOR OUTDOORS
STEP OUT TO MUSIC
YOUTH CLUB PROGRAMMES

YOUTH WORSHIPPING
YOUTH CLUB SONGS
YOUTH CLUB ACTIVITIES
YOUTH CLUB CONTEST QUIZZES
TEAM QUIZZES
BIBLE QUIZ BOOK
EDUCATION FUN FOR YOUTH
WHAT-TO-DO, FOR UNDER-15's
KNOWLEDGE FOR THE GROWING
    BOY
PRAYERS FOR YOUTH CLUBS

SWIMMING

THE COMPLETE SWIMMER
THE SWIM BOOK
BOYS' AND GIRLS' SWIM BOOK
SWIMMING AND WATERMANSHIP
THE BOOK OF SWIMMING AND
    DIVING
THE BOYS' BOOK OF SWIMMING
THE GIRLS' BOOK OF SWIMMING
SWIMMING, DIVING, AND LIFE-SAVING
SWIMMING IN TWELVE LESSONS

HOW TO SWIM CRAWL
MODERN SWIMMING AND DIVING
SWIMMING
MODERN SWIMMING
SWIMMING – HOW TO SUCCEED
LEARN TO SWIM
HOW TO TEACH SWIMMING
HOW WELL DO YOU SWIM?
SWIM
CRAWL AND BUTTERFLY SWIMMING

MISCELLANEOUS

PILGRIM BY PLANE
EVERYBODY'S BOOK OF HOBBIES
UNIVERSAL BOOK OF HOBBIES
THE HOME ENTERTAINER

SELF-HELP FOR THE VIOLINIST
ICE AND ROLLER SKATING
SEEING EUROPE CHEAPLY
I WRITE FOR A LIVING

JUVENILE FICTION

THE AFRICAN HEIR
TALES OF PENDLECLIFFE SCHOOL
TOL THE SWIMMER

BOYS OF PENDLECLIFFE SCHOOL
THE PENDLECLIFFE SWIMMERS
TOM THUMB TALES

NOVELS

THE WEIR BODY MYSTERY
THE CHANNEL TUNNEL MYSTERY
THE MALTA MYSTERY
MEDITERRANEAN MYSTERY

THE VENETIAN SWIMMER MYSTERY
PLAGUE PANIC
DIAMOND DUEL
WAR ENDS AT MALTA

The Youth Club
Ideas Book

SID G. HEDGES

METHUEN & CO LTD
11 NEW FETTER LANE LONDON EC4

First published 1964
© *1964 by Sid G. Hedges*
Set in 'Monotype' Baskerville
by the Gloucester Typesetting Company
and printed in Great Britain by
T. H. Brickell and Son Ltd
Gillingham, Dorset

Preface

Youth club workers are always needing fresh ideas which will help towards the never-ending problem of programme planning. The popularity of my *Youth Club Programmes* is evidence of this. What is here provided is a similarly packed volume, but one less formally arranged. Instead of a series of weekly outlines as given in *Y.C.P.* here is a sort of general storehouse of different material, classified under headings each of which can yield a stimulating diversity of possibilities for every sort of club occasion.

Sectional divisions are, of course, just an arbitrary convenience, and many included items might just as properly be placed elsewhere.

Young people increasingly manage their own affairs in successful clubs of today, and it is hoped that this book is such as the leader will not only use himself but confidently hand to his members.

S.G.H.

Bicester

Contents

Contents

SECTION ONE

Indoor Features

In this section are items each of which can form the special novelty or chief attraction of a club evening, indoors. Such a feature gives the opportunity for all club members to be together in a worth-while common interest, perhaps for half-an-hour.

PLEASE, I NO SPEAK

This is a novel miming-acting feature in which individuals volunteer in turn to play a part at one end of a room, which might be 'the stage'. The audience is divided into two sections, which are competing teams. At the outset only the leader is at the 'stage' end. He explains the procedure and rules of the contest to the teams:

It is to be assumed that the volunteer who presently will come forward is in a foreign country, unable to speak a word in the language of the local people – the audience. In order to communicate with them he must therefore mime, gesture, or act, until they understand what he wishes to communicate. The leader will have instructed him what message he is to try to get across. As soon as any-one in the audience, from either team, guesses what is being 'said' he will dash forward and whisper it to the leader. If he is right he scores 2 points for his own team. If all attempts to interpret the miming fail the 'actor' returns to a seat, forfeiting 1 point for his team. Before letting a volunteer see the slip of paper the leader will announce 'the setting'.

So the thing begins. The leader has a number of slips of paper, on each of which is written a single instruction. About eight are enough for half-an-hour. Here are exam-ples, the 'setting' which is announced to the audience is given in brackets:

2

1. (In a city) Where is the railway station?
2. (By a river) Can I swim here?
3. (At a bookstall) I want some picture postcards.
4. (On a country road) There's been a car accident round the bend.
5. (At a small hotel) I want a single bedroom for two nights.
6. (In a shop) How much is this?
7. (In a village) Where can I get a meal?
8. (In a street) I've lost my little girl.
9. (In a town) Where is the police station?

The leader calls for a volunteer. Anyone, from either team, may dash forward. The setting is announced, and he is allowed to read the first slip. He then tries to communicate it. He can make noises, but must not mouth any words – to prevent lip-reading. If all those who come forward whisper a wrong solution and he fails to get his message across, he loses his point and sits by the leader – where he cannot give anything away to his team. Another volunteer comes forward; is shown the same slip, and tries afresh. If, however, the first actor successfully scores his 2 points then he returns to his team, and a fresh volunteer is invited who is shown the next slip.

Be careful not to award 2 points until the exact message is guessed.

No-one should be allowed to 'act' twice, as long as there are others wishing to have a go.

THEN AND NOW

Get in an outside speaker who will simply talk about what life was like for him (or her) when he was in his teens.

Let him be entirely factual and personal, so that his listeners get a clear picture of home and community life several decades, or maybe half-a-century ago. What taboos ruled then; what were the challenges, opportunities, conventions, dress, codes of morals? Don't let your speaker moralize, or draw any conclusions or parallels with the present day. All the comments must come from your young people in later discussion groups.

Instead of the familiar personalities of your own usual helpers, try to get fresh, outside leaders for these groups, who will have heard the preliminary talk, and be interested in finding the group's reactions to it. Group leaders need not talk themselves, and must not be impatient with preliminary silences. It will be surprising if some group member does not get going before long, drawing parallels between ways of getting excitement today and how the guest speaker got it in his own time. There may soon, also, be expressed revolt against the way adults exploit teen-agers. You should all gain a lot in tolerance and understanding.

YOU KNOW IT

Four quiz lists are put up, widely separated about the room. Four blackboards will serve if you have them. Alternatively write on poster-size white paper, using charcoal or a heavy marker – which can be bought from art shop or stationer. Every person is provided with pencil and paper, and about fifteen minutes can be allowed. Papers, with competitors' names written on, are then collected and marked. Finally, results are read out – it is best to give the score of every player. Here are four sample lists – items should be written separately one underneath the other; the answers, of course, will stay with you:

1. *Hidden Animals.* I am rather nervous (rat); Please be a very good girl (beaver); Try to add it up (toad); Ten blue pigeons (pig); I made Eric sing (deer); Churchill, famous Englishman (mouse); Alec owes me it (cow); She was early, he came late (camel).

2. *Jumbled Towns.* FICFDRA (Cardiff); LOONBT (Bolton); NNLLCOI (Lincoln); GNOTHIBR (Brighton); TSEBAFL (Belfast); BUHDENRIG (Edinburgh); AHGSNITS (Hastings); LLPOOERVI (Liverpool).

3. *Join Up.* (Here are pairs of syllables, wrongly linked. It is required to fit proper parts to each other so as to form eight complete words). PAR-ART; CAR-HER; HAM-KEY; FAT-SON; SET-WIT; OUT-PET; DON-TEE; IMP-LET (Parson, Carpet, Hamlet, Father, Settee, Outwit, Donkey, Impart).

4. *Quiz.* Who is patron saint of Wales? (St David); How many books has the New Testament? (27); What is bronze? (Alloy, copper and tin); Who wrote *Peter Pan*? (Barrie); What did Kreisler play? (Violin); What did Sam Weller's father do? (Drive stage coach); Whose home is the Mansion House? (Lord Mayor of London); In a limerick, which line rhymes with third? (fourth).

DRAWING BY EAR

One person is asked to sit on a chair in the centre of the room. At the end of the room, behind this person's back, another volunteer is facing a blackboard, with chalk in hand. Neither person must turn round, but continue facing in opposite directions all through. The seated person is handed a slip of paper on which the name of some object is written, or he can better still be given the actual object – like a kettle, pocket knife, glove, shoe. He then goes on – without allowing any clue to escape him as to what the object is – to give the 'artist' directions which should enable him to produce the correct drawing. The result is usually astonishing.

SKIN YOUR EYES

This 'observation test', which takes at least twenty minutes, can be tried periodically – thereby testing whether your group's powers of observations are improving with practice.

The thing is easily arranged. Have four tables spaced out along the middle of the room; on each table have four objects. At a given moment all are permitted to walk round the tables, examining the sixteen objects – but *without touching any of them*. Allow ten minutes for this detailed examination, then cover up and let all sit in a ring, each person with pencil and paper. Down the left-hand side of each paper must be the numbers 1 to 16, with sufficient space at each number to allow the answers to two questions (a, b). You then begin to ask questions, allowing sufficient time for all to write their answers. But when the 32 questions have been asked and answered each person passes his paper to the right-hand neighbour. Now you read out the correct answers, and every competitor ticks off the correct replies on the paper he is holding, totalling up at the end. Papers are then passed back to their owners, so that each can announce his score.

Here is a suggested list, and the questions to be asked: **1.** Shoe (*a*, Was it left or right-foot; *b* Was the heel most worn on the inner or outer side); **2.** Framed photograph (*a*, Was the person looking to her right or left; *b*, What sort of necktie was he wearing); **3.** Hymnbook (*a*, What was the number of the hymn on the right-hand page; *b*, How large was the first letter in each hymn – did it go down to the second, third, fourth line); **4.** Half-crown (*a*, What letter of what word is at the middle of the bottom of the coin; *b*, How many crowns did you see); **5.** Addressed envelope (*a*, What was the postmark; *b*, Which word in the address was wrongly spelt); **6.** Ballpoint pen (*a*, Colour of the ink; *b*, Was there a metal band round the middle); **7.** Dandelion leaf (*a*, What kind of leaf was it; *b*, Was it torn on the right or the left side); **8.** Purse (*a*, Was it open or closed; *b*, Was it standing up or lying down); **9.** Open matchbox (*a*, What was the name on it; *b*, How many matches were inside); **10.** Dishmop (*a*, Was it dry or wet; *b*, What colour was the handle); **11.** Squash bottle (*a*, Was the top screwed right down; *b*, How far up the label did the contents reach); **12.** Comb (*a*, Were the teeth all the same size; *b*, How many teeth were missing); **13.** Cup (*a*, Was it cracked; *b*, How many different coloured rings were round the rim); **14.** Page from an exercise book (*a*, How many lines were there; *b*, Did it have rounded corners); **15.** Gramophone record (*a*, What was the make; *b*, Who was the conductor); **16.** Bunch of keys (*a*, How many keys were there; *b*, What, beside keys was on the ring).

POP ARTISTS

If twenty members take part in this they can compete individually; if there are forty they may work in pairs – the whole thing is easily adjustable. Your folk may prefer to work singly or in pairs, at their own choice, and the duration of the contest can depend on the interest it evokes, which will determine the time you allow for the actual drawing work.

Your preparation consists in compiling a list of 'pop song' titles – take some care over this, for they must be titles likely to be known to your members, yet it is best not to let competing members know about them beforehand. Assuming you are planning for twenty, your list might provide something like this: **1.** She loves me; **2.** Cruel to me; **3.** It's all in the game; **4.** I'm telling you now; **5.** I'll never get over you; **6.** I don't want to stay; **7.** Please don't ring off; **8.** Sweets for my sweet; **9.** Just like Jane; **10.** You don't have to cry, baby; **11.** Even roses have thorns; **12.** Dance on; **13.** Hot it up; **14.** Au contraire; **15.** Apple tree; **16.** The cruel sea; **17.** I'm confessing; **18.** Still; **19.** Wishing, I'm wishing; **20.** Singing for you.

Next, each competitor must be provided with a fairly large sheet of drawing paper – pages of cheap drawing books will serve. The sheets are very plainly numbered in their corners, corresponding with the numbers of your list. To each drawing sheet is attached, by clip or staple, two slips of paper On the first will be written the name of the song corresponding to the number. For instance, on the drawing page numbered **12** the first slip will bear the name *Dance on*. The second slip will be headed 'solutions', and will have the numbers **1** to **20** written down the left

8

side – perhaps ten on the front and ten on the back, to reduce the size of the paper – against these numbers competitors will later have to write such titles as they can find. One last requirement – pencils for everyone, if they can be coloured so much the better.

Now to begin. Let your competitors scatter about the room, and give to each one drawing paper with its attached slips. Each person takes of his title slip – making sure that no other competitors see it – and proceeds to make a drawing which represents that title. For *Dance on* it might be a solitary dancing couple in the club with others collapsed and exhausted round them; the canteen empty; the clock showing 2.30 a.m.; the dancers' shoes worn out. When the drawing is completed you affix it to the wall with cellotape. The competitor meanwhile will have retained the second slip. When other drawings are similarly put up on the wall he begins the second stage of the contest, examining each drawing, trying to guess what it represents, and if he is successful writing down the title against the appropriate number on his Solutions list.

When all drawings are up and all competitors have had adequate time to make the round of them and fill in as many titles as possible, the slips are collected and marked, or alternatively you may read out solutions from your original title list, with competitors marking their own papers and announcing their scores.

TEENAGERS IN AN ADULT WORLD

Autumn is a time of unusual strain for those who are leaving school for full-time work, or transferring to more nearly adult places of education or vocational training. A club can very usefully make special efforts to be practically helpful at this time.

Get a suitable adult to lead discussion, and ask questions on such matters as: attitude to older people; the unrealised strains and difficulties of adults; holding the balance between saving and spending, study and rest, work and leisure; social contacts and personal development; how important is dress; how much must the individual conform in society; idealism and realism; what is a good citizen, and so on. But be sure to let the young people themselves air their own problems and discoveries.

HOLIDAY REVIEW

Group holidays are becoming increasingly popular, and while summer experiences are fresh in mind is the best time to discuss plans for the future.

Go to some trouble with preparation so that you have plenty of factual material available. After the introductory speakers, have free discussion, then try to sum up finally with definite proposals for next year.

So begin by getting several people, preferably club members, though this is not essential, to describe different types of group holidays in which they have shared during recent months, and which suggest possibilities for your club in the future. One might speak of how several friends hiked on the Continent; a second could recount experiences at a Church Holiday Conference; a third might tell of adventures on a hired houseboat; another might describe pony trekking – and so on.

Remember that your general aim is to discover ways of spending *group* holidays, so that you do not want mere reminiscences of ordinary solo experiences. Having made this clear, let general discussion break out. This should have to do with how any group scheme might be tackled by your club. You may guide the talk occasionally by interjecting such questions as: What is the ideal number of people? Should there be someone in charge, and what sort of person should he be? What would be the most suitable length of such a holiday? How much would it be likely to cost? What time of year would be most suitable? Would any particular qualifications be necessary? Could preliminary preparation be planned during the winter – language practice, for example, if the trip is to be abroad?

You can also throw in suggestions other than those which have turned up in the talks; exchange holiday with a group from some other country; voluntary service at home or abroad; boating-camping trip; help with an archaeological dig; youth hostelling; achievement tests; cycle touring.

You may decide to discuss the matter again when further information along particular lines has been obtained. Church organisations and Education Authorities are usually able to give helpful advice.

QUICKWITS CONTEST

Get two or more teams and see which can first solve the following problems.

Survival. Suppose you were confined in a room with only a bed and a calendar. In order to survive what would you eat and drink? (Springs supply water; the calendar has plenty of dates.)

Spell Test. This has three stages. You ask your members to spell 'joke' – and, as all probably shout out together, you can award no points. You then ask them to spell 'folk' – with similar result. Finally ask for 'the white of an egg' and deduct a point from all who say 'y-o-l-k'.

Baby Duck. Mummy Duck, Daddy Duck, and Baby Duck went for a swim. Baby Duck said: 'Aren't we four having a lovely time?' Why did he say four? (Baby Duck wasn't very good at counting.)

Time-Speed. Two cars of the same make start out simultaneously to drive along a new motor way for a distance of approximately 80 miles. They travel at the same speed and under exactly similar conditions, yet while one does the journey in 80 minutes the other takes 1 hr and 20 mins. Why is this? (The times are the same.)

Cutting Time. You have a 30 ft length of rope, and with a rather blunt knife wish to cut it up into 1 ft lengths. How long will it take you to complete the job if one minute is occupied in achieving each cut? (29 minutes.)

Mixed Family. It was a mixed family – each daughter had the same number of brothers as sisters, and each son twice as many sisters as he had brothers. How many girls were there, and how many boys? (Four girls, and three boys.)

Odd Ties. Mr Grey, Mr White, and Mr Brown were drinking coffee together. One was wearing a brown tie, one a grey tie, one a white tie. 'Isn't it odd,' said the one with the white tie, 'not one of us is wearing the tie which matches his own name, although our three ties are of the same colours as our three names.' 'You are right,' exclaimed Mr Grey, glancing at his companions, 'yes, it's odd.' Which man was wearing which? (Mr Grey couldn't have had white, since he was answered by the white tie man, and grey would have matched his name, therefore he was wearing brown. White couldn't have been worn by Mr White, so he must have had grey – which left Mr Brown to wear white.)

FLEXIBLE MINDS

This interesting feature is adapted from a type of test used in some American high schools, intended to discriminate between minds most adapted for arts courses and those best suited for science. An object is displayed and those taking part are invited to suggest the various uses to which it might be put – a vivid imagination and flexible mind obviously helps, but so does the cold scientific appraisal.

Split your people into small teams, supplying each with a pencil and paper, and group them round the room. Put your first object at the centre, on floor or table, and allow several minutes for the teams to list the uses to which it could be put. Then call a halt and let each team read out what they have. You can award one point for each satisfactory suggestion. Follow with a second object, dealt with in the same fashion – and so on. Suppose your first thing was a brick – it might produce such answers as the following: to keep a garage door open; to help a short girl reach a tall shelf; a toy for a child; to start up a builder's business; to block a car wheel on a hill; to fill a hole in the road; to make a stepping stone across a brook; to heat in the oven and warm a bed in winter; to stand a mousetrap on; to prop up a photograph; to use for measuring; to block a hole in a fence; to help sink a sack to the bottom of a river.

All sorts of objects can follow – stick, duster, key, washer, blanket, board, liquid.

OF COURSE YOU KNOW

Ideally for this feature you should have two Africans and two Asians visiting your club – students would be just right. But, of course, such may not be available, and the evening may still be most interesting with any other nationals from other countries.

Each of the visitors is previously asked to have ready six questions about his own land, the answers to which he assumes your members know – this last point is most important.

When the speakers have been introduced each in turn puts his questions to your young folk, and they give what answers they can – it is quite possible that your visitors will be surprised to find that they just cannot answer at all! Anyhow, when the 'home team' have shown their knowledge (or lack of it), the visitor expands the answers from his own personal experience, in just a minute or two.

Finally, you can question your visitors on a few points which you, in your turn, genuinely expect them to understand.

CONVERSATION NIGHT

It might be three Jamaicans, or six Americans – or whatever group belonging to another country you are able to get.

14

Supposing it is half-a-dozen Americans. You seat them in a row and face them with half-a-dozen of your English members. All the rest form an audience and listen to the sort of general conversation which passes between the two groups. Each group in turn, through any one spokesman, asks a question of the other group, who are free to answer it as they like. The English might begin: 'What is pumpkin pie like?' Or the Americans could start off: 'Why do you have such awful weather?'

Just go on until it's time to stop!

STANDBY QUIZ

This is a team contest game which you should always have on hand; it is such a useful standby when some other planned feature falls through or when you just want to fill an odd half-hour. Equipment is simple enough. First, twenty cards – playing-card size or smaller – on each is written one letter, or one of the four pairs: A, B, C, D, E, F, G, H, I, J-K, L, M, N, O, P-Q, R, S, T, U-V, W-Y. The following list is also needed. It can be simply written into a book or you may put each item on a separate card – which in play will give the advantage that you can shuffle the cards instead of reading always in the same order from your list. Here are the quiz-questions: Something used in sport: A fish; A song; A word of eleven letters; Something white; An occupation or trade; Something from the grocer; A fruit; Something connected with a wedding; A character from a book; A word of ten letters; Something connected with the seaside; A composer; From the ironmonger; A flower; Something to drink; A book title; A word of 9 letters; Something connected with sea travel; A boy's name; Something from a draper; A tree; Something to eat; A foreign town; A word ending with B; Something which goes into the making of clothes; A girl's name; Something from a china shop; An animal; Something you couldn't eat; A river, lake, or sea; An exclamation; Something which helps to make music; A sportsman or athlete; A tool; Something seen in a theatre or concert hall; Two opposites, like *high and low*; Something you would like to abolish; What you would like to be; Something from the greengrocer; Part of a motor; Something which makes a noise; A country; A word ending in *ion*; A London street or place; Something from the stationer; Part of a ship or boat; Something made of metal; A county or state; A word in which this letter occurs three times; Something you can ride on; What you wouldn't like to be; A hobby; Something made of wood; A word ending in W; Something that grows; An author; Something connected with air travel; A television or radio celebrity.

To use your *Standby Quiz*, seat your two teams, and place yourself at a table in front of them, with your quiz list and pile of letter cards – or two piles of cards – before you. Read out a question, and turn up a letter card announcing the letter. Thus: 'Part of a motor, beginning with C', or 'A word ending with W, beginning with J or K'. Give one question to the appropriate member of each team in turn, and write down the scores – two points for a correct answer, one point if the right person fails to answer but another member of his team succeeds.

To get a second round, when all the questions have been given, simply shuffle the letter cards and start afresh.

SPENDING SURVEY

It is often said nowadays that many young people have far too much money. Certainly teenagers are the avowed target of very clever advertising and high-pressure salesmanship. Yet broadly, the young people who are most affluent are usually those with least knowledge of the variety of things money can buy for them. A club programme or special feature can usefully be built around this fact. Begin with an introductory talk, listing the things which are familiar – bicycle, motor cycle, camera, tape recorder, record player and records, transistor set. They are all so hackneyed and familar; are there not other fresh and interesting ways of spending money? After this it may be well to split into discussion groups and see which can bring back the most striking set of proposals. It could first be agreed that something like a total expenditure of £50, or £2 weekly should be understood.

Here are the sort of things which might emerge: travel holidays; original paintings – which can be had for as little as a couple of pounds; books of outstanding quality; *objets d'art*; philately, numismatology; climbing and exploring; gliding and flying; boating; music study.

TEAM QUIZ CONTEST

The following set of questions should last for half-an-hour. They are planned in five groups, each with three pairs of matching questions. The groups are of progressive difficulty. You might have girls competing against boys and team members could be seated in order of ages, so that a thirteen-year-old might answer Group 1, a fourteen-year-old Group 2 and so on. But probably you can ignore ages, with members all enjoying the challenge of increasing difficulty. Each question must be put to a single person. If he answers correctly he scores 2 points; if he fails, anyone in his team can give the answer, scoring 1 point.

Group 1

TEAM A (1) On which side of the road should you walk when there is no footpath? *Facing the oncoming traffic.* (2) What is ditchwater said generally to be? *Dull.* (3) Two sports or games beginning with P.

TEAM B (1) Give two reasons why it is dangerous to cross the road near stationary vehicles? *You cannot see traffic; and drivers cannot see you.* (2) Where do people often go 'out of the frying-pan'? *Into the fire.* (3) Two sports or games beginning with R.

Group 2

TEAM A (1) From which country are the fleetest horses said to come? *Arabia.* (2) How many sides has a modern threepenny piece? *Twelve.* (3) Two towns beginning with S.

TEAM B (1) To what land does the caribou belong? *North America.* (2) What is often on the back of a halfpenny? *A ship.* (3) Two towns beginning with T.

Group 3

TEAM A (1) What is the holy book of the Mohammedans? *The Koran.* (2) What highwayman rode the horse Black Bess? *Dick Turpin.* (3) Is it true or false that Ceylon is not really an island? *False.*

TEAM B (1) What book properly lies between the Old and New Testaments? *Apocrypha.* (2) What famous person rode a horse in Coventry? *Lady Godiva.* (3) Is it true or false that the River Jordan flows in a northerly direction? *False.*

Group 4

TEAM A (1) 'The Unfinished Symphony' was composed by – ? *Schubert.* (2) Standing on a concrete floor, how can you drop a fresh egg five feet so that it does not even crack? *Drop it from some greater height so that it falls 5 feet before meeting the floor.* (3) When is midsummer day? *June 24th.*

TEAM B (1) Who wrote Madam Butterfly? *Puccini.* (2) The two duellists stood one facing east and other facing west. How could they see each other without turning round? *Easily – they were facing each other.* (3) When is Lady Day? *March 25th.*

Group 5

TEAM A (1) Why, when you put on a slipper, do you always make a mistake? *Because you put your foot in it.* (2) Who were Aztecs? *An ancient Mexican people.* (3) In which Shakespeare play do two men fight in a grave? *Hamlet.*

TEAM B (1) Prove that a horse has six legs. *It has forelegs in front and two behind.* (2) Who were Boers? *Dutch-descended South Africans.* (3) In which Shakespeare play does a lady disguised as her twin brother fall in love with a duke? *Twelfth Night.*

FASHION PARADE

Give no warning beforehand, for improvisation and inventiveness will then have fullest scope. Announce that the girls are now invited to take part in a fashion display.

They will be allowed five minutes to go out to their cloak-room and decide what they will wear (if possible let a woman helper accompany them, to smooth out any difficulties or arguments). Each girl in turn must later parade before the audience of the other members, with a changed hair-style, wearing some sort of scarf, and carrying an *accessory* like umbrella or bag.

Two friendly adults, preferably man and woman, should have been invited to act as judges. The competitors should draw numbered slips of paper, and so be called on in proper rotation. Each one will parade – walking down the middle of the large ring of onlookers; turning, and walking back again. Of course, it will be poise and deport-ment which will be the main consideration for the judges, who may award as many points as they choose out of ten to each competitor. The scores of the two judges will then be added, so that the placings can be decided and announced. The girls can come back into the room to hear the judgement. Unless there are a large number of competitors it may be a good plan to announce only one winner – so as to avoid hurting the feelings of those who do not get placings.

I KNOW WHAT I LIKE

This works best if members previously have no inkling of what to expect. They are seated, perhaps facing a table or a curtain, and then are suddenly faced with three large objects placed on the table or revealed when the curtain is drawn. They are then invited to discuss – one at a time – which of the things they prefer, and why. All sorts of objects can be used, providing they are of the same general type. Three small tables, for instance of completely different styles. Kitchen utensils, in which colour and design can be discussed as well as practical utility; calendars, vases or ornaments; potted plants.

DISC QUIZ

You will need a lot of records for this, and the more widely you can borrow the better so as to get real diversity of taste. So have not only music – classical, light, popular, dance, religious – but just anything else you can get. But don't have new records, for you propose to play just excerpts from them, starting and stopping anywhere.

One of the pleasantest ways of running a feature of this sort, is to have your people work in pairs, but they can just as well be in two or three larger teams, or competing as individuals. You provide pencils and paper, or let them call out, as you please. The thing is to play a short excerpt from each record in turn and let the listeners determine what it is. If no-one should get the full answer, like 'the Fourth Brandenburg Concerto' scoring 2 points, then 1 point might be given for 'something by Bach'.

It is of course possible to tape your excerpts beforehand, and so save a lot of trouble putting on and taking off records.

Alternatively, let each listener have pencil and paper; number the pieces played, and let each write down titles, composers, and so on. This method always works well with current, popular records.

HANDWRITING EXPERTS

It is usually assumed that character comes out in handwriting. The handwriting expert, like Sherlock Holmes, can read much more than character – perhaps age, sex, occupation as well. So here is an interesting club feature enabling all to try their skill in making deductions from samples of writing.

The major preparation consists in collecting several lines of handwriting from about twenty diverse people. You may do this in part by collecting letters you chance to have and masking all but a few lines, or by getting specially written samples from a variety of people. Each sample is then clearly numbered – and you are ready to begin.

Every club member taking part has a pencil and paper. All sit in a ring. You yourself have a key list, which might run as follows: **1.** Elderly unmarried lady. **2.** Artist. **3.** Children's nurse. **4.** Doctor. **5.** School teacher. **6.** Plumber. **7.** Young wife. **8.** African. **9.** Undergraduate. **10.** Grocer. **11.** Schoolgirl, aged 15. **12.** Old-age pensioner. **13.** Lawyer's clerk. **14.** American tourist. **15.** Child, aged 7. **16.** Music teacher. **17.** Minister, aged 70. **18.** Schoolboy, aged 10. **19.** Retired draper. **20.** Bricklayer.

You ask all taking part to write the list of people, one under the other – but you do not disclose the numbers belonging to them. Then your samples of handwriting are passed round slowly, letting each one get on three or four people ahead before starting off the next. So everyone examines each specimen in turn, and writes its number against the person in the list who is judged to have written it. When all have finished you read out your own key list, and at the end discover who has made most correct guesses.

A MEDLEY MATCH

This is a team contest likely to last about half-an-hour.

Each team consists of three to five people, and there can be three to six teams, each with its own selected Captain. The Leader controls the whole thing; announces and explains items; sees that there is no waste of time, which can cause lack of interest; stimulates rivalry and excitement by having scores called out at frequent intervals. He can be helped by a Timekeeper and Scorer, if both are available; otherwise he must run everything himself.

Things required: a table for each team; paper and pencil for every competitor; a copy of the same book for each team – a hymnary will serve; a large book or any convenient object, the exact weight of which you know; four threepenny-pieces for each team; a card no larger than a postcard, for each team; a penny for each team; chalk; a foot-rule or tape measure.

The Match may consist of the following nine features.

1. Pencil skittles. Chalk a cross, near table end, and stand a short pencil on it – this is the skittle. Competitors have to slide a similar short pencil from the other end of the table, hoping to knock the skittle over. When the Leader has called 'Go' play goes on non-stop. Each member of a team in turn has one go, and the Captain keeps count of how many times the skittle is *knocked* over. At the end of two minutes the Leader calls 'Stop', and asks the Captains for their scores, so that the teams can be allotted places.

2. Wardsback Write. Each team sits round its table. Each Captain has pencil and paper, and a book – it might be *Sunday School Praise*, open at the Preface. At the word

'Go' the Captain begins writing, beginning at the last word of the page and spelling backwards – thus 'service' would be 'ecivres'. In about 30 seconds the Leader calls 'Change', and papers are passed on to the next team members, who continue the writing. Each person in turn has a similar spell, and when the full teams have had their turn scores are made according to how far they have got.

3. Weight Guess. Each team member has pencil and paper. The book or other object is out at the front. No. 1 from each team comes forward; judges the weight; returns and writes it on his paper. Then No. 2's do the same – and so on until all have tried. Captains finally add all the weights of their teams, and divide the total by the number of team members – so that placing scores for correctness can be decided.

4. Threepenny Building. Run this like *Wardsback Write*, each player in turn being allowed 30 seconds to stand the coins up edgeways on top of each other. The best number achieved is counted – it will probably be 3 or 4. When all are finished the Captains report their totals, and points are awarded by the Leader.

5. Card Toss. A chair is placed for each team, and each member in turn tries to toss a card on to it from a chalk mark on the floor, about 4 ft away. The thing goes on non-stop like *Pencil Skittles*.

6. Push Penny. A circle, about 4 in across, is marked at one end of each table. From the other end a penny is knocked, as in *Shove Ha'penny* play – half of the coin first overhanging the edge and this then being hit by the fleshy base of the thumb. Continue non-stop as in *Pencil Skittles*. A penny must be entirely inside a circle to score.

7. A.B. Huddles. Teams huddle round tables. In two minutes they write down as many words as they can beginning with AB.

8. Eye Measurement. Team members come out in turn, holding their forefingers at what they judge to be 18 in. apart. The Leader measures, and calls out the plus or minus inches to Captains. Captains reckon final scores at the end.

9. Under the Bridge Twice. A hectic team relay race to finish. Each member runs up the room; goes under the table front to back; turns right and goes under table from end to end; then back.

In reckoning final score the 'possibles' for each feature should be made approximately the same. In items 1, 5, 6 scoring is limited only by time, and a team may get a dozen points. But in the other features only placings can be recorded. It is advisable therefore to multiply all these by 3 or 4.

TOP-TEN TOPICS

Let all your members sit comfortably, supplied with pencils and paper. Then ask them to write a list – one under the other – of the following topics as you read them out: Sport, School or Job, Religion, Current Affairs, Friends, Records and T.V., Politics, Homes and Parents, Amusements, Books and Reading, Dress, Holidays. Without consulting each other it is now required that each shall decide which are the most frequent and popular topics of conversation.

A figure 1 should be put in front of the first favourite, 2 before the next, and so on down to ten. Topics other than those in the list can be added or substituted if desired in their numbered order of preference.

Collect the papers and during canteen or refreshment interval let one or two competent people analyse the results. The simplest way is for one person to have a well-spaced list of topics. He acts as scorer, adding the appropriate placing number against each as the numbers on each paper are read out by his fellow. Scores are then totalled, and the order of precedence is shown – the topic with the lowest total being, of course, first in popularity.

Members reassemble and the finalized list is read out. Comments are then invited. It is not difficult to get talk going on 'Why I do, or don't, agree'. This will especially be so if either girls or boys preponderate and so a topic chosen by one is forced high or low on the list despite strong dissent from of the opposite sex.

A variant – TOP-TEN PEOPLE

This is not very different. In introducing the feature the leader should make clear that the aim is to discover which ten people are, in the view of club members, most important or useful to the world. In these introductory remarks it should be your aim to raise questions rather than answer them. Can a national politician benefit mankind generally? Can an Asian or an African be of importance to the western world? Is a man who thinks as valuable as a man who acts? Are there any women who have world-wide influence? Are entertainers really important? Does a person need to be linked to an organisation if he is to exert wide power? Are the greatest people those who are well-known?

Then just mention a few names at random, to set their minds working – the more varied the better.

Allow your members about ten minutes to list their 'top-ten people'. There is no need for any numbering or order of preference. Afterwards collect the papers and work out the placings during the refreshment interval. To do this you will write down the names one under the other as they are read out from the papers by your assistant. When a name recurs you put a mark against it, so that finally you can discover how many votes have been gained. When you reassemble read out the resulting top ten – and invite comments on, 'Why this name is on my list'.

NOUGHTS AND CROSSES QUIZ

This can be an absorbing event for two competing teams; it is a quiz contest to which is added the fun of a noughts and crosses game. First mark a blackboard as shown on page 28.

Seat your teams in facing rows – there may be six or eight in each. One lot are *Noughts* the others *Crosses*. You, as leader, stand at the front, with chalk, duster, quiz list. Each team in turn starts off a bout. The first member of the starting side is allowed to choose any of nine subjects, and is then asked a question relating to it. If he can answer, his cross (or nought) is written into that space. His opposite number of the other team then chooses a subject, and tries to answer the resulting question – getting his own mark in that space if he is successful. The next pair of opponents follow – and so the contest goes on until one team has its three noughts or crosses in line horizonally, vertically, or diagonally, and wins the game. You then rub out the marks, and the new bout begins, the next player in turn on the side which has just lost being allowed to start off.

SPELLINGS	POPS	PAIRS
MIXED	PEOPLE	HOME
WHICH	GAMES	TOPICAL

Here are half-a-dozen matching pairs of questions for each of the subjects shown: *Spelling* – **1.** insatiable; parenthesis, **2.** paralysis; facsimile, **3.** dinosaur; catarrh, **4.** hypocrite; symphony, **5.** queue; furlough, **6.** eligible; illegible. *Pops* – **1.** Pop song beginning with D; S, **2.** T; L,

3. Title including boy's name; girl's name, **4.** Title of four words; three words, **5.** Title which asks a question; title which makes a statement, **6.** Title which ends with S or A; T or D. *Pairs* – **1.** Damon and – (Pythias); Hero and – (Leander), **2.** Boswell and – (Johnson); Dante and – (Beatrice), **3.** Gilbert and – (Sullivan); Gog and – (Magog), **4.** Darby and – (Joan); Antony and – (Cleopatra), **5.** Ananias and – (Sapphira); Cain and – (Abel), **6.** Ruth and – (Naomi); Romeo and – (Juliet). *Mixed* – **1.** Where is your nearest football ground; swimming pool, **2.** What is Sanscrit (ancient sacred language of India); What is Aries (first sign of zodiac, constellation Ram), **3.** Word beginning with GN (gnash, gnat, gnaw); with GH (ghastly, gherkin, ghost), **4.** What Bible book follows Psalms (Proverbs); John's Gospel (Acts), **5.** Which is poisonous, box tree or beech (box); larkspur or lilac (larkspur), **6.** Where are Hebrides (west of Scotland); Scilly Isles (west of Land's End). *People* – **1.** Artist of today; author, **2.** Poet; sculptor, **3.** Composer; conductor, **4.** Actor, screen actor, **5.** Editor; publisher, **6.** Columnist; foreign correspondent. *Home Things* – **1.** Two household things beginning with C; B, **2.** Beginning with S; D, **3.** Two foods grown in garden; two warm drinks, **4.** Housework ending in ing; beginning with W (washing); Ending ing; beginning S (sweeping), **5.** ing, D (dusting); ing, I (ironing), **6.** Two foods not in tins; in tins. *Decide* – **1.** Verdi was: French, *Italian*, English; Chopin is famous for: marches, *waltzes*, songs, **2.** Parthenon is at: Paris, Rome, *Athens*; Bodleian Library is at: Paris, Liverpool, *Oxford*, **3.** Berkshire's county town is: Oxford, *Reading*, Winchester; County town of Sussex is: Brighton, Portsmouth, *Lewes*,

4. First English cricket was played about year: 800, *1200*, 1600; Cricket's main growth was in: eighteenth, *nineteenth*, twentieth century, **5.** Khartoum is capital of: *Sudan*, Egypt, Kenya; Suva is capital of: *Fiji*, Samoa, Borneo, **6.** Eddystone Lighthouse is near: Newcastle, Edinburgh, *Plymouth*; Severn Tunnel is near: Stoke, Salisbury, *Bristol. Games* – **1.** Check, belongs to (chess); Puck (ice hockey), **2.** Huff, (draughts); Cannon, (billiards), **3.** Two games beginning with A; B, **4.** Two with C; D, **5.** Board game which isn't judo (ludo); isn't frontgammon (backgammon), **6.** Two bat-propelling-ball games; foot-propelling-ball. *Topical* – **1.** Current topic in Parliament; Today's front page news, **2.** Famous foreigner in news; Foreign country happening this week, **3.** Recent statement by notable person; Woman in the news, **4.** Town in the news; Two countries linked in news, **5.** Current interest in France; U.S.A., **6.** Topical happening in Africa; Asia.

WHAT I BELIEVE

Suppose your club is attached to a Methodist Church, then it will be good for your members to be trained into tolerance and appreciation of other sects – Baptists, Catholics, Plymouth Brethren, Congregationalists, Anglicans, and so on. Try inviting a representative of another denomination to come and give his point of view. His job will be not to win over your own members but to make a fair statement of 'What I believe', and to deal with questions and inquiries afterwards. It may not be easy to find able exponents, but if you can the effort will be worth-while and the result will almost certainly be to make your young people realise the fundamental sameness, rather than the superficial differences, of the various branches of the Christian Church. If practicable, a member of the Society of Friends will usually make a good start for a series of this sort.

You might afterwards go on to other faiths, if you can get the people – Jewish, Moslem, Buddhist, Hindu.

POLITICAL ROUND-UP

The introduction of politics into the youth club ought not to be shirked, but discretion and planning are important. Party politics can be avoided, but all the matters which come into the field of political action and discussion have a legitimate place. There are many ways of devising such programmes. For instance: *What the Parties stand for* – let individuals or groups prepare and give summaries of what the various parties profess. It is fairly easy to get leaflet and information from local political organisations. Alternatively let a representative of each party make a five-minute statement; *Mock election* – carry it through like the real thing, preceded by Candidates' speeches. A local Returning Officer may advise helpfully; *In the News* – let chosen members read or report about matters of current politics, and follow with discussion; *Political Quiz* – questions on current affairs, names of office holders in the Government, personalities in world politics; *Distinguished Visitor* – would your Member of Parliament come and talk on 'My Job as an M.P.'? *The Wider World* – Get some knowledgeable person to introduce talk on some such subject as Disarmament, the Common Market, the United

Nations, controlled or unrestricted immigration; what does a Free World mean; Religion and Politics.

OPERATION 'EMERGENCY-PLANNING'

This is a novel type of open discussion, giving especial scope for imagination and originality. You, as leader, will introduce it, and guide its course. You first outline the emergency then, acting as chairman, put pertinent questions and so elicit the views and ideas of your group – who have to find a quick and satisfactory solution to the dilemma in which they find themselves.

It might be: 'You are informed that, due to unexpected developments, the first rocket can and must be launched to Mars within the next week. Your group is to make immediate and complete planning for the expedition, with the whole resources of the nation at your disposal. Four or so of your members are to go.'

Then you start the discussion off – remembering to use only questions: What are the first steps? How shall the rocket team be chosen? What equipment? What provisions? If the trip occupies three months each way what special problems arise? If Martians are found how shall contact be made? If communication with them is achieved what can they be told about Earth people? Does religion come into the matter, and how? What sort of promises could you make them on behalf of Earth people which would suggest to them that to establish fuller contacts would be beneficial to the Martians?

Such a discussion, of course, would be likely to take up all the available time on any one club evening, but the general planning of the feature can be used for other rather similar topics. For instance: You are all in a plane, which crashes, with no casualties, in remote Brazilian jungle – how shall you organize yourselves and behave towards the ferocious jungle folk, with the prospect of having to stay perhaps for a month?

Or: You have all escaped from a shipwreck to a desert island – how shall you plan your group's Robinson Crusoe existence?

FUN WITH A TAPE

The tape recorder programme here envisaged may begin as fun and go on to become a bit of serious research and continuing usefulness to the club.

Begin with a Sounds Quiz, the preparation for which you can do beforehand. Simply record a diversity of sounds preceding each by a spoken number, so that you have a list of the 'answers', and also so that members taking part in the quiz may list their own solutions if necessary. The sort of sounds you may get on your tape could be: a book dropping to the floor; a plane passing overhead; a tap being turned on; an envelope being pushed through a letterbox; a lid being put on a saucepan; beating up an egg; a nose being blown; a window being shut; money being put into a meter; scrubbing; telephone dialling; a lawn mower in action; a saucepan boiling; a cat purring; chopping wood. Individuals or teams may compete in guessing at these sounds.

A further development can be, experimenting in ways of producing particular sounds. If you have a special interest in drama you may evolve your techniques for particular sound effects – whistling or blowing close to the microphone for wind sounds; dropping dried peas on to various surfaces for rain and hail; flattening piano bass notes, with sustaining pedal on, for thunder – or shaking iron sheet; clapping two pieces of wood for walking sounds or clip-clop of horses. Club members may compete in producing effects by their own chosen methods – and these can be played back and judged on their merits. Similarly individuals can speak dramatic words or phrases, in private, and have the results adjudicated in public.

BIBLE QUIZ CONTEST

For Two Teams. Here is a set of questions enough to last for half-an-hour. They are planned in five groups, each with three pairs of matching questions. The groups are of progressive difficulty. In taking the contest use up the first pair of questions from each set before going on to those numbered 2. Each question must be put to a single person; if he answers correctly he scores 2 points; if he fails anyone in his team can give the answer, scoring 1 point.

Group 1

TEAM A (1) How many disciples had Jesus? *Twelve.* (2) Spell: Adam. (3) Over which river did Joshua lead the Israelites? *Jordan.*

TEAM B (1) Name three of the disciples. (2) Spell: Eve (3) Over which sea did Moses lead the Israelites? *The Red Sea.*

Group 2

TEAM A (1) Two names of Bible people beginning with A. (2) Give the 'twin name': David and –? *Jonathan.* (3) A

34

New Testament woman called Magdalene – what was her other name? *Mary.*

TEAM B (1) Two names of Bible people beginning with B. (2) Give the 'twin name': Cain and –? *Abel.* (3) A Queen in the Old Testament who gives her name to a book. *Esther.*

Group 3

TEAM A (1) In which Bible book do you find Paul? *Acts.* (2) 'The Lord is my Shepherd' – where is this found? *Psalm* 23. (3) Paul was first called by another name, what was it? *Saul.*

TEAM B (1) In which Bible book do you find Daniel? *Daniel.* (2) Who said 'Blessed are the peacemakers?' *Jesus.* (3) When do we first hear of Paul – before; at the same time; or, after the life of Jesus? *Just after Jesus.*

Group 4

TEAM A (1) What great and terrible choice did Pilate make? *He gave up Jesus to be crucified.* (2) How old was Jesus when he first went up to Jerusalem? *Twelve.* (3) The Lord's Prayer – How was it first given? *Jesus taught it to his disciples.*

TEAM B (1) How did the Good Samaritan's choice differ from that of the priest and the Levite? *He stayed to help; they passed on.* (2) How old was Jesus when he began his public ministry? *Thirty.* (3) What Old Testament boy heard God speak to him? *Samuel.*

Group 5

TEAM A (1) Give two other names for Jesus. *Saviour, Master, Messiah, Lord.* (2) Jesus taught in synagogues –

where else – give two other places. For example: *seashore*, *boat*, *hillside*. (3) Spell: Exodus.

TEAM B (1) Give two other names for God. *The Lord, The Almighty, Jehovah, The Highest*. (2) Jesus healed lepers – what other sort of people did he heal? For example: *blind, paralysed, dumb*. (3) Spell: Genesis.

For Competing Couples. Four couples can most conveniently compete in this (if you want more then the number of questions here given must be varied). At the first round the first members of each couple must answer in turn. For a correct answer 2 points will be awarded. If a competitor cannot answer, his partner can reply and score 1 point. In the second round the second member of each couple answers first – and so it goes on. Be sure to have an alert, careful scorer. Here are questions sufficient to make the feature last about half-an-hour: *Occupations*. **1.** What were the disciples James and John? (Fishermen); **2.** What was David? (Shepherd); **3.** What were Aquila and Priscilla? (Tentmakers); **4.** What was Matthew? (Tax Collector); **5.** What was Samuel? (Priest); **6.** What was Pilate? (Roman Governor); **7.** What was Barabbas? (Thief); **8.** What was Joseph in Egypt? (Ruler – Prime Minister). *Words*. **1.** Make a joyful *blank* unto the Lord all ye lands. (Noise); **2.** For God so loved the *blank* that He gave His only begotten Son. (World); **3.** God is our *blank* and strength. (Refuge); **4.** And though I bestow all my *blank* to feed the poor. (Goods); **5.** Blessed are the pure in *blank*, for they shall see God. (Heart); **6.** Father, *blank* them for they know not what they do. (Forgive); **7.** Blessed are the *blank* for they shall obtain mercy. (Merci-

ful); **8.** Remember the Sabbath Day to keep it *blank*.
(Holy). *Spelling.* **1.** Canaan; **2.** Galilee; **3.** Exodus; **4.**
Daniel; **5.** Psalms; **6.** Joshua; **7.** Elijah; **8.** Genesis. *Names
beginning with.* Two names of Bible people or places beginning
with: **1.** N; **2.** P; **3.** S; **4.** G; **5.** M; **6.** C; **7.** D; **8.** B. *Free for
All.* In the following un-numbered items the first competi-
tor to answer scores a point. *Odd One, Out.* Martha, Mark,
Mary. (Mark was a man – Mary and Martha were
sisters – Mark has one syllable); John, James, Job, the
Bible books .(Job is in Old Testament); Jordan, Jerusalem,
Jericho. (Jordan is a river); Sinai, Simeon, Sennacherib.
(Sinai was a mountain). *Hidden Bible People.* Isn't her cape
terrible. (Peter); She rode a motorbike. (Herod); The
running man drew nearer. (Andrew); Earache leaves you
weak. (Rachel). *Pot-Shots.* Open your Bible cleanly at:
Matthew, Psalms, Exodus, Acts. *Jumbles.* (Bible books)
GSKNI (Kings); KUEL (Luke); HAISIA (Isaiah); MHTOTIY
(Timothy). *Mixed Set.* **1.** Put this right – Elijah cured
Naaman of leprosy. (It was Elisha); **2.** Who were the
parents of Cain and Abel? (Adam and Eve); **3.** In which
Book do you find Jacob? (Genesis); **4.** Name five New
Testament Epistles; **5.** Name four places visited by Jesus;
6. Two Bible names ending in M or N; **7.** Where did
Jesus take His disciples after the Last Supper? (To the
Garden of Gethsemane); **8.** Two Bible names ending
in H.

KIBBUTZ PLANNING

One of the most striking features in modern Israel is the
kibbutz (plural *kibbutzim*) – a communal collective settle-
ment, mainly agricultural, but often with industrial enter-

prises. The population of a *kibbutz* may be from 50 to 2,000. All property is collectively owned and work is organised on a collective basis. The members give their labour and are supplied in return with housing, food, clothing, education, culture and social services. There is a central dining room and kitchen, communal social centres and stores, but individual living quarters. The *kibbutz* is governed by the General Assembly of all its members.

Having explained to your club members what a *kibbutz* is, let them imagine that they are to form one in some suitable piece of open country known to you all. Then try to work out all the details of organisation. Be severely practical, allowing for no help or gifts whatever from the outside, other than the piece of land itself. Plan the day to day life, with its problems of food and clothing. It may help to assume the inclusion of a certain number of young married couples in order to obtain men of wider skill and experience. Try to envisage and cope with every aspect of life in such a self-governing community, both in labour and leisure.

Clearly this project cannot satisfactorily be dealt with in a single hour of one evening – it may be good to have one introductory session at which several small groups be formed to deal with various aspects of *kibbutz* life – provision and maintenance of accommodation and premises; food production; how money is to be obtained and spent; rules and regulations; general duties and privileges. A second session could hear reports from these groups, and a third general assembly could evolve a general constitution and scheme of living.

EASTER BONNETS

The girls produce the bonnets; the boys judge them. Announce one week that the girls are each required to bring an 'Easter bonnet' or hat on the following club night, and judgement will be made as to which is most striking and original. The hat can be some decorated or renovated old model; something freshly made from odds and ends; or something quite farcical, like an upturned pudding basin with a fringe of clothes pegs, or a saucepan with an artistically-trailed handle.

On the night the girls bring their 'creations', and one of them is chosen to 'model' the lot in turn. The hats are numbered and announced – 'No. 3, pale-fawn satellite with meteor fringe' (the basin, of course); 'No. 7, Winston' (hat with cigar-like protuberance); 'No. 11, Keep your distance George' (pillow or cushion balanced on the head).

Each boy, not knowing who has devised each hat, awards up to 5 points for each one exhibited, writing the number he has given to each hat – and the scores are totalled – or the papers can be collected and counted. The winning girls can be called out, each wearing their particular creation – and they can be told that the club will permit them to walk home wearing them as a reward.

DEBATE CONTEST

This needs arranging some weeks ahead, for it is a debating contest between teams of three, and each trio will need to prepare and rehearse. The three taking part consist of: The Proposer – who introduces the Resolution; the Seconder, and another Speaker – who adds, or sums up. Topics should be chosen by teams.

On the Contest evening two or three adjudicators sit together, each marking independently, and the teams make their appearance one after another. The adjudicators come together – perhaps during canteen interval – to summarize and decide, then announce their verdicts and reasons afterwards. A single judge, of course, can do the job.

Such debating contests can be organised with other clubs, on a knockout basis, with fixtures at each other's headquarters.

MISSIONARIES

Split your members into small groups. Then – without warning – spring this on them.

First explain the situation. They are to imagine that they have been flying across Africa, and their plane has crashed, without anyone being injured. They find themselves in remote jungle and in a small village where a white man has never even been seen, though it happens to be ruled by a witch doctor who has a knowledge of English which he has passed on to the villagers. (Of course it's improbable, but it suits our present purpose.) The party must content itself with living in the village for several months. Seeing the backward, superstitious condition of these poor people, your party is naturally anxious to introduce Christianity to them.

At this point you send your groups into huddles. Each will have 10 minutes to decide on just what plans of action and argument they would make to help enlighten the villagers. At the end of the allotted period the spokesman of each group reports.

It is helpful if the club leader and one or two other people represent the villagers, and so give their judgement on which proposed programme is most likely to have the desired effect on them.

ARE THESE THE FACTS?

Discussion can easily arise from the following provocative statements:

The average family is not a friendly democracy, in which parents and teenage children share views. Parents lay down the laws without consultation, thus creating rebels. Worse still, when they have made rules they haven't the interest, or the courage, to insist that they are kept. So there is neither co-operation nor firm rule, and the gulf between parents and children remains unbridged.

A second unbridgeable gap is between those at work who have plenty of money, and those still being educated, who have none.

Youth's chief use for money is to make himself, or herself, attractive to the opposite sex. To think oneself unattractive is the greatest of hardships.

Religion, in its real sense, is the only inspiration that can bridge gulfs and put into life a power that makes all merely personal desires seem unimportant. It has not necessarily much to do with churches.

BRAINS TRUST

These can be planned in several ways. Outside people can be brought in if desired, but it is more helpful to use this method as a pleasant way of getting members themselves to express opinions in front of others. Four is a good number for the Trust. They can sit prominently, at the front, and deal with questions which are handed in written on slips of paper – or which have been handed in beforehand. The Club Leader can be *Question Master*, and it is his duty to give out the questions at discretion, so that each of the Brains Trust in turn has a chance to open up the talk. The questions sent up should usually be matters of opinion rather than fact. Merely to ask for information or test knowledge on particular facts belongs to the Quiz Corner – the interest of the Brains Trust is in the differing views held on a particular topic.

An alternative method of planning the Trust is to have the questions asked direct from the audience – though this is not usually so satisfactory. But this method can be used in still another form of Trust. When all are in their places, push back four to one end of the room, and announce that they are to be the Brains Trust. One question can be asked of each, by any of the audience, or the first two can deal with the first question, and the third and fourth members with the second. When they have finished the Leader instructs the entire ring to move round four places – thus four new people come into the 'Trust' seats, and in turn face the questions.

MY SORT OF PICTURE

The more of a surprise this feature is the better it will go. When the time comes let your members seat themselves as the audience, reasonably near to the display point – then place before them, or uncover on the wall, three reasonably large pictures of contrasting styles – it should not be difficult to borrow these. The first might be something Italian or Dutch, classic or representational art; the second an impressionist painting, perhaps French; the third a modern abstract painting, fairly incomprehensible at first sight. You, or some invited person, then give a brief dissertation on each style of painting – and then invite club members to give their own views, and say which they prefer. Begin by asking one or two who can be relied on to respond well, and then it should not be too difficult to get others to follow. The stronger and more personal the views expressed the better.

IT REMINDS ME OF

Public speaking ability is immensely useful, and every device is worth trying by which club members can be got on their feet to express themselves. In this particular method a theme or topic is announced, and each person in turns says 'It reminds me of . . .' and recounts some incident or recollection from his or her experience. Of course, those who wait longest to speak have most time in which to think; but against that, those who speak first escape the danger of having someone else use what they would have liked to say. If this is pointed out to your members their reluctance to start will be lessened, and you may be able to sit in a ring, with each in turn opening up the new subject. If a subject appears to fizzle out, drop it and start another.

Here are the sort of things which might spark off the speeches: A farmyard; Singing in the dark; A bad day at school; Lemonade; A brass band; Water which is very cold; Cows; A partly-built house; Thunderstorm; Missing, or catching, a train; Cats and dogs; Not having enough money; Noises.

SPELLING BEE

This can be either a team or individual contest. One way of arranging it is for the leader to work from a dictionary on the spot, but it is probably better to have a prepared list of words. Here is one: Tabernacle, formula, medicine, possession, impromptu, emulsion, ancient, annuity, illegible, eligible, icicle, separation, paralysis, earache, eavesdrop, ruffian, precipice, poultice, prairie, conjuror, crocodile, crocus, florin, education, universe, trespass, shampoo, rescued, refreshment, papyrus, laughable, gnu, eclipse, cannibal, neighbour, nephew, heathen, excursion, consequence, baggage, rumour, sacrifice. Score one point for each correct spelling. Do not pass on words when an error is made.

A SLICE OF LIFE

This is a way of opening up talk about real-life problems of the teenager. Its special value lies in making them try to understand the points of view of other people.

Suppose you start with 'getting a job'. You first ask volunteers to take the rôles of: The Boy, Father, Mother, Schoolmaster, Careers Adviser, Prospective Employer. Then you dramatise and improvise the various scenes – Boy talking with Father about leaving school; Mother joining in, with her own angle on what she would like her son to do; talk with Schoolmaster; interview with Careers Adviser; more discussion at home; visit to Employer. The important thing is that each shall try to think and speak in the way of the person represented. General talk and comments may follow.

It is not difficult to plan other problems and situations: Should I attend Church? Should I choose my own clothes? What aspects of sex create problems? How should I use my spare time? And so on.

GROUP MIMING

Split your players into groups – there can be up to a dozen in each. They sit in separate clusters, leaving the end or the middle of the room clear – unless you chance to have an actual stage on which the ensuing performance can be presented.

The producer has a prepared list of 'scenes', perhaps: Boxing (2 males); Typing (1 girl); Riding a Tandem (a pair); Shop Assistant and Customer (2); Car Learner-Driver and Coach, with nervous passenger (3); Employer, Secretary, Applicant for job (3); Wedding Reception, Couple and Guests (any number); Boat Race (9).

One or more judges sit at the side of the room. A 'scene' is announced, and each group in turn sends out their representative actors to perform it. Marks, and adjudicating comments, can be given as desired.

Be sure that each group in turn has to start first, for obviously those who play the same scene afterwards will benefit from observing the previous performances. Take care also that everyone inside a group sooner or later is given a chance – or compelled to take one.

TRANSFORMATIONS

This is a word contest testing quick wits and knowledge of

words. It can be played by individuals, couples, or small teams – just three or four in a team is usually best. Pencils and paper are needed. The leader announces two words of the same length, and the team is required to transform one into the other by a chain of intermediate words each of which differs from its neighbours by only a single letter. For example, *lead* can be transformed to *gold*, one letter at a time being changed, thus – *lead, read, road, load, lord, ford, fond, bond, bold, gold*. But that is unnecessarily long and a much better version is: *lead, load, goad, gold*. Here are other examples: *dry* to *wet* – dry, day, say, sat, set, wet; *fast* to *slow* – fast, past, pest, peat, seat, slat, slot, slow; *rain* to *fine* – rain, rail, fail, fall, fill, file, fine. Four-letter words are best; five letters give more trouble – *snake* to *tiger*, snake, spake, spare, spars, stars, sears, seals, sells, tells, tills, tiles, tiler, tiger.

Other possibilities: *hard* to *soft*; *fish* to *chip*; *girl* to *boys*; *swim* to *walk*; *play* to *work*; *black* to *white*.

Award 3 points to the player or players who finish first; 2 points to those who are next; 1 point to the third. Similarly at the end, give 3, 2, and 1 point to the shortest 'chain' of words.

EMERGENCIES

Split into small teams, and let the teams separate into groups so that none can overhear the discussion of any other. Then announce an 'emergency' and let the groups have a few minutes to work out exactly what they would do to be helpful. A spokesman for each group can then be asked to report – so that all the rest can hear. Warn each spokesman not to vary his report in view of what any previous speaker has said. If you have several 'emergencies' in succession it is best to have each group in turn reporting first. Here are possible 'emergencies'. Others can easily be devised which apply to your particular premises or circumstances:

Two motor bikes collide just outside. You hear the crash, and see machines and riders sprawling in the road.

Smoke is coming from the windows across the street; the house is on fire.

On entering your club premises you find the toilet awash through a blocked drain.

The club leader has an attack of giddiness, and faints.

On arriving at the club you find the door has been broken open; it looks as though a thief has entered.

At camp there has been a drowning accident and parents are naturally anxious, though you all want to continue bathing.

WHAT'S MY LINE?

There are many ways of planning this. If you have no more than a dozen club members they can be split into two competing groups. With a larger number you can have four or five as Challengers, a similar number as the Panel, and the rest as the Audience. Each Challenger then does his mime, and the Panel members make their guesses – ten wrong guesses gives the point to the Challenger, and the next Challenger is called out. Thus it is a contest between Challengers and Panel as to which can score most points.

But, usually, the best way to plan this feature is to have just three or four sitting at the front of the room, well away from the Audience so that the clear space between them serves for the miming dramas. It is helpful to have a Chairman or Compère in charge. In turn each of those at the front steps forward on to the 'stage', having decided on some trade, occupation or profession, which is supposedly his and mimes his job or some characteristic series of actions which represents it. A *carpenter* might lift an imaginary plank on to a stool and saw it across. A *chimney-sweep* could be adjusting his rods and pushing up his brush; a *draper* unrolling material and cutting it off; an *air hostess* handing round meals on trays, and so on. When the mime is done, or during it, the audience make their guesses. Anyone who guesses right goes to the front and sits in the end chair, while the previous 'actor' goes back to the Audience. A mime can be called for several times. The person in the first chair always mimes next, having moved along when it was vacated, and the newcomer goes into the last chair.

BLACKBOARD QUIZ PROGRAMMES

The technique of the Blackboard Quiz is simple enough. Two teams of about six sit facing each other. Between them a blackboard is propped between two chairs so that each team faces one side of it. Duster and chalk are provided for each team. The Leader calls 'Number Ones' to him and whispers something – he might say 'Witch'. He then announces: 'It is a person', and as the two dash back to their respective sides of the board and begin to draw, the teams see which can first call out what the drawing is intended to represent. The first to be right scores a point. 'Number Two' artists then go to the leader for a fresh instruction. Be sure that Number Ones clean the board before returning to their seats.

Don't take a full set of subjects together; jump from one group to another.

Here are three full programmes:

Programme 1

People – **1.** Witch, **2.** First man on the moon, **3.** Florence Nightingale, **4.** Henry VIII, **5.** Chairman of the local council, **6.** A local personality.

Places – **1.** Oxford, **2.** New York, **3.** South Pole, **4.** Local suburb, **5.** Ceylon, **6.** Main street.

Buildings – **1.** Eiffel Tower, **2.** The house that Jack built, **3.** St Peter's, **4.** Local church, **5.** Big Ben, **6.** London Bridge.

Nursery Rhymes – **1.** Hey diddle diddle, **2.** Jack Sprat, **3.** Little Jack Horner, **4.** Little Miss Muffet, **5.** Georgie Porgie, **6.** Tom, the Piper's son.

Hobbies – **1.** Gardening, **2.** Stamp collecting, **3.** Knitting, **4.** Fishing, **5.** Record collecting, **6.** Camping.

Special Days – **1.** Bonfire night, **2.** Mothering Sunday, **3.** Birthday, **4.** May Day, **5.** Cup Final, **6.** Annual Concert.

Programme 2

Flowers – **1.** Pansy, **2.** Dandelion, **3.** Tulip, **4.** Bluebell, **5.** Rose, **6.** Orchid.

Countries – (no maps must be drawn – letters and figures are never permitted) – **1.** Spain, **2.** U.S.A., **3.** France, **4.** China, **5.** Russia, **6.** Ghana.

Words and Phrases – **1.** Thank You, **2.** Which is the way to? **3.** How much? **4.** Please, **5.** Where is the nearest doctor? **6.** I want a currant loaf.

Lessons – **1.** Dressmaking, **2.** Shorthand, **3.** Metalwork, **4.** Scripture, **5.** Dancing, **6.** Cooking.

Towns – **1.** Washington, **2.** Baghdad, **3.** Manchester, **4.** Edinburgh, **5.** Pisa, **6.** Peking.

Shakespeare plays – **1.** Hamlet, **2.** A Midsummer Night's Dream, **3.** Julius Caesar, **4.** The Merchant of Venice, **5.** King John, **6.** The Tempest.

Programme 3

Occupations – **1.** Barber, **2.** Greengrocer, **3.** Plumber, **4.** Typist, **5.** Chemist, **6.** Doctor.

Bible Stories – **1.** Daniel in the lions' den, **2.** Friendship of David and Jonathan, **3.** Prodigal son, **4.** Israelites crossing the Red Sea, **5.** Jonah, **6.** Paul and Silas in prison.

Sports – **1.** Polo, **2.** Water ski-ing, **3.** Judo, **4.** Lacrosse, **5.** Croquet, **6.** Gliding.

Songs – **1.** Old folks at Home, **2.** The Happy Wanderers, **3.** Tipperary, **4.** Passing By, **5.** Waltzing Matilda, **6.** The Grand Old Duke of York.

Famous Happenings – **1.** The first man in space, **2.** The first woman to swim the channel, **3.** The conquest of Everest, **4.** The Battle of Hastings, **5.** Stanley meeting Livingstone, **6.** Columbus discovering America.

Famous Buildings and Places – **1.** Piccadilly Circus, **2.** Gibraltar, **3.** The Empire State Building, **4.** London Zoo, **5.** The Louvre, **6.** Venice.

UNDER OBSERVATION

Three *Suspects* sit side by side, facing all the rest – who can be divided into teams of three or four – like an audience. It is the business of the teams to observe the *Suspects* closely, noting and reporting whatever changes they see in them. So, after a half minute, all the teams go outside – or turn about so that their backs are towards the *Suspects*. These latter immediately make some change in position and sit motionless again. The audience teams come in, or turn round, and try to see what changes have been made. There must be no talking or comment, but any individual spotting an alteration must dash at once to the Referee and report in a whisper. If he is correct he scores a point for his team. When any team has three such points – because each of its members has spotted the same thing – the round is over, and all the teams turn away once more while the *Suspects* make a second change. So the game proceeds as long as may be desired.

Here are suggestions for alterations by the *Suspects* – who at the outset will have been sitting with feet together and right hand resting on left: **1.** Feet apart; **2.** Hands on separate knees, feet unchanged; **3.** Arms folded, legs crossed; **4.** Right hand holding left; **5.** Arms crossed, feet together; **6.** Chairs turned sideways, feet tucked under.

The Leader or Referee will instruct the *Suspects* for each change. To make things more difficult the *Suspects* need not all make the same changes. And, teams can write down what they observe jointly, instead of scoring as individuals.

WHAT WOULD YOU ANSWER?

(Here are extracts from letters received by me when I was editing a

'Can I help you' column. As they deal with real life problems they can form excellent topics for discussion. Just read an excerpt to your teenager group and invite them to provide an adequate answer.
S.G.H.)

'I've a vague idea my heart doesn't function according to plan, and I have always been denied boyish pastimes. It's pretty hard seeing your fellows indulging in rough and tumbles and being unable to join in. So I'm moody, inclined to mope about, and generally make myself a killjoy. My pals have deserted me. When I go out, which is rarely, I feel ill and depressed. Cheerful customer aren't I? Nothing of the true, hardy Britisher, yet to look at me you would think I was in the best of health. Can you give me any tips?'

'I am 16, and wonder if you could help me. For some time I have felt as if an anchor is attached to me, slowing me up. I find it difficult to get friends of either sex. My memory seems very poor and I have great difficulty in concentrating, in fact I seem to be an outsider.'

'I am only 14 but lately I've been thinking, while at home with flu, about the tripe that some of the chaps at school call jokes when it's just a lot of filth. When I go back next week I'm going up to one particular fool and if he tries to crack any more of his jokes I'll knock his teeth down his rotten neck, in fact I think I'll do it anyhow. Could you give me some advice as to what to do when I get mixed up in this sort of talk, and also what to do when some lout, or louts, asks me for a fight. I am a moderate boxer, and always accept. Is this right?'

'I like dancing, and so do all my girl friends because we learn it at our secondary modern school. But it isn't allowed in our Church, and even my parents don't approve. My boy friend isn't keen either, but that is because he doesn't dance and he really would like to learn. I should like to leave our Church youth club and go to a town one where they can dance. What do you think?'

'Some months ago I used to work with a firm, and I absolutely hated the job and did not know whether to hang on to it until I got another job or chuck it up straight away. I decided to finish there and then. Now I have an excellent job with endless prospects, but I can't help thinking perhaps I was lucky and it was really silly to be so quick to act. Do you think I was?'

'I am 16 and my parents have never told me any of the essential facts of life. I am at a boarding school where I get a rather warped idea. Could you tell me of a book putting the facts plainly, all those I have seen advertised, by doctors, seem to be for adults only. But I think I should be able to read something definite, learnt in a decent manner. Or who could I ask?'

'I shall be 16 in March and am in a 5-year apprenticeship. Is there a fund I could pay into that would ensure me a pension when I retire? Of course that is looking rather far ahead, but I should like to know, and it is good to think ahead isn't it?'

'My ambition is to be an author and I am at work on a story now. I am only 17 and have not much experience or knowledge of writing. The book is nearly finished and I have written it in the third person, so that no character in the book actually speaks. Is this all right? Is there any chance of getting my book published? Who would I write to about it? If published would I get paid for it?'

'My mother is out at work and she gets precious little time off. I live with my auntie and grandpa. Naturally I visit Mother as often as possible and I have work to do both for her and at home. However, Mother and Auntie have very different ideas and their advice and orders in my affairs often clash. This puts me in a dilemma, so could you please tell me where my obedience is primarily due – to my mother or the people I live with, or when it is advice on my own affairs should I use my own discretion? All my letters are opened, and I do not want any unpleasantness.'

'I was going to say I hate being a South African but perhaps I'd better change it to, I dislike being one. A friend of mine has just come back from England and says that all the time he was there he was ashamed of being South African because of the way people think about us. But we can't help being Whites and what can we do about it anyhow?'

'I am at present in an office and don't like it, and I have always had an itch for sketching. Could a person like me become a cartoonist, and how should I set about it. It is good to have ambitions, isn't it?'

'This may not be quite in your line but could you tell me something that really will remove blackheads from the skin?'

'I shall be 17 next month and am shy at talking to people. So I read a lot and am very solitary, everywhere I go I go alone and it is getting on my nerves. I've no friends to confide in, to keep me company, to talk to. It seems that I am at the foot of a deep ravine and I must climb out and up the mountain, and gather friends, money, self-confidence, and the other things that make a successful life. But how can I? If I could talk to people instead of being silent; if I could make some money to help my parents; if I could believe in myself. I could go on for hours with if – if – if. How do I get a "backbone" instead of a "wishbone"?'

'I am a sixth-former and a 9-year-old boy has made me the object of his hero worship and is at times rather a nuisance. What can I do about him? I have another friendship problem. Two years ago I made one particular friend. We liked each other very much but this last year (he's 17) he's changed completely. His conversation is full of girls, films, gangsters, and it's sickening. He is now a bully and is making himself hateful all round. He seems hurt by my refusals to share schemes which are certainly not honourable. And yet I can't dislike him, I feel sure he's decent enough at the bottom. Ought I to end the friendship, or go on waiting? Not the easiest part of it is keeping up the pretence at home that we are still great pals. To admit the truth would somehow hurt my pride. But I think mother would understand, ought I to confide in her?'

'There are a lot of West Indian and other coloured people where I live, and I've got some good friends among them. But my mum gets worried that I might marry a coloured girl. "If you do," she says, "you'll never see the end of all her relations, and you'll never be really happy again." I don't think I shall ever marry anyhow, but I think she's wrong don't you?'

'There is a girl in our school who comes from a dreadful home. It is shabby and broken. Her parents get drunk and quarrel. This girl wears awfully old and poor clothes, and sometimes even smells dirty. Boys sometimes make fun of her, but most in the school just leave her alone. I'm really sorry for her, but what can I do to help?'

'Three months ago my mother died. I felt that the end of the world had come, but I went and saw our club leader at home, and his talk helped me a lot so that I got to feel better, for I saw how God can be kind even when He seems cruel. But my father isn't the same, and I am very worried about him. He just mopes about every night when he's finished work, and won't do anything or go anywhere or speak to anybody. He says that God has punished him. He won't go to church any more, and he won't talk with our club leader or the minister. He can't go on like this, can he?'

'I am a girl of just on 17 and I've been married six months. My husband is in a bank and has been moved to a new town. We have a new little house, but we don't know anyone and all the neighbours seem to look down on me. I am so lonely I could die, and I am always wishing I could be back at school where I had plenty of friends. I still love my husband, and I feel it's wicked to have thoughts like I do, but can't help it.'

'One of our club girls has been saying that nowadays things are different and every girl has a right to do what she likes with herself, even to sell herself for money if she wants to. Plenty do it if they can't get a good living any other way, and it's recognised that plenty do it for love without getting married anyhow. All this sounds awful to me, but when she's talking I can never think of what to say. There must be some answers and I should like to know some good ones.'

'I have a boy friend. We are both 15, and we love each other. When we are alone and get very close to each other and he touches me I feel I would do anything for him, I sort of go to pieces and don't want to stop, though my conscience tells me not to. Am I very wicked, and can you give me any advice?'

'I stammer badly, and have never been out with girls in case they laugh at me. I am 18. I have been to a speech therapist and he didn't really help. Is there any way in which I could find a girl who wouldn't mind my stammer?'

'I'm a boy of 18, but my parents seem to think I'm still a kid. I have a room of my own, to sleep in, but it isn't private in any other way. My parents walk in any time without ever knocking, and I know my mother often goes through all my drawers and cupboards – to tidy up she says. But my father also opens all my letters if he is down first. This doesn't seem right, but what can I do about it, for they are good parents in other ways and I wouldn't like to hurt them?'

Outdoor Features

Summer Possibilities	Clue Hunt
Swim Party	Summer Hockey
Hike Planning	There and Back
Off-beat Hikes	Cycle Rally
Sausage Sizzle	Cycle Treasure Hunt
Wiener Roast	Night Duty
Tramp Soirée	Spending Spree
Wool Gathering	From Here to There
Documentary	Window Spotting
Litter Blitz	Yo-yo

These are of the same general type as in Section 1 except that now they are for outdoor use.

SUMMER POSSIBILITIES

Plan well ahead for summer. There are so many possibilities available to individuals and to groups of teenagers, and information can be quickly forthcoming from Church and Inter-denominational bodies, local Education Authorities, Travel Agencies. It might be a good idea to put up some sort of list on your notice-board in order to get club reactions; then you can obtain fuller information as required. Here is a practicable list of the sort of things which might appeal.

Cycling and Camping – In Britain or Normandy or Brittany; *Canoeing Expedition* – on Thames or Wye or other convenient river, or across to France; *Field Path Exploration* – with ordnance map guidance; *Pony Trekking*; *Hiking* round the coast, or inland, or in Holland or in the Black Forest; *Sailing Holiday* on the Norfolk Broads; *Bird Watching* – almost anywhere between here and Iceland; *Climbing* – in Wales, in England, in Scotland; *Exchange Holiday* – with German or Dutch or Norwegian young people; *Individual Adventure achievement*; *Work Camp* – of the sort sponsored by the British Council of Churches; *Archaeological dig*.

With such preliminary information, choose the right sort of evening for an outdoor occasion and have a general discussion on the sort of things the club can do during the ensuing months.

SWIM PARTY

Swimming is especially enjoyable and helpful if you can plan it as a club – you need the pool or stretch of water exclusively for yourselves so that you can put through some sort of programme. If the swimming bath belongs to the Local Authority see if you can get a reserved hour – this is often permitted at off-peak times providing you guarantee sufficient attendance, or payment. If you go to open water, try and arrange that you get it as much as possible to yourselves by choosing the right time, or by just keeping clear of the most popular spot. But be quite sure, of course, that conditions are safe and suitable.

If you are planning a series of swim parties, as distinct from one rollicking occasion, try to ensure real tuition.

Have tests – beginner – 10 yds; badge (if you can get one) – 25 yds; proficiency – 100 yds breast, 50 yds back, a plunge or header and so on. Encourage your members to perform at least half-a-dozen different strokes in good style; to surface dive; to tackle life-saving; to explore fancy swimming, including tandem and group work; to dive.

Races, rescues, romps, all have their place – but don't over-organize. Allow plenty of leisure and free time, while ensuring that everyone is encouraged to develop their general watermanship and distance swimming ability, whenever you take a 'club dip'. But don't be tempted to relax precautions. Danger is always present if bathers enter the water within two hours of a meal, or venture out too far, or dive in shallow or crowded water, or push other folk in or pull them under.

HIKE PLANNING

Two or three young people, not younger than fifteen, can tackle a worthwhile hike together, with an overnight camp. Fifteen to twenty miles may do for boys, or rather less for girls. To give maximum value the hike should begin and finish away from familiar home ground, and the route should be worked out beforehand, aided by a proper map.

If the hike is to be a club project or a test, the young people should not know any details beforehand, but simply be handed clear instructions based on agreed map references. Instructions might be given in this sort of form: Start from road and track junction Map Reference 526142, and keep to east of canal. Describe the general area (such description and other information to be collected should be written in a log-book – which will have much importance in the final assessment of the hike). What is interesting at Map Reference 514169? Describe land between MR 502205 and MR 527108. Camp in area MR 534233 (Get permission. Give detailed description of site.) Travel to road junction MR 553315 and travel east. Sketch the church. On reaching MR 572263 take shortest and easiest route to MR 582228 – and finish.

OFF-BEAT HIKES

Doing things together, at off-beat times, is always good fun. Do such things just occasionally, when the weather is right, and your members will be reminiscing nostalgically for a long time afterwards.

Sunrise Hike. Get up well before daybreak, and watch the sun rise as you hike.

Breakfast Hike. Start off, fairly early, for a cheerful hike, and cook breakfast at some pleasant, previously agreed site.

Supper Hike. Get most of the hike over first, so that you are not too far from home when you settle in the growing dusk and cook – or just eat – a much-welcomed supper.

Moonlight Hike. With or without supper, and with or without a break to identify stars and constellations.

And on one hike drink tea, at dawn, made from melted snow, which must of course be boiled first.

SAUSAGE SIZZLE

Nothing can equal sausages for outdoor occasions when a bit of improvised cooking can be fitted in. And a good name helps so much. *Sausage Sizzle* really sets the mouth watering. You can impale them on bits of stick round a picnic or camp fire. Or, of course, you can equally well have them indoors on the gas stove or electric ring. Whatever else you fit in to fill the evening let the Sausage Sizzle be the peak of enjoyment.

WIENER ROAST

'Barbecue' is often overworked nowadays and 'Wiener Roast' can be a fresh name for very much the same sort of thing. The *Wiener* will simply be a sausage – which need not come from Vienna.

So, at your chosen outdoor spot, get your hot fire of glowing embers over which members can roast their skewered sausages. Or do the lot in a large tin. All the fun which goes with the camp-fire will naturally follow on.

TRAMP SOIREE

Ideally this should be on a fine warm evening, concluding with some sort of barbecue supper. Whether in a field or wood, farm building or barn, or even at home in club premises, the basic requirements will be the same. Chief of these is that everyone should come dressed as a tramp; the older and more disreputable the clothing the better.

Hiking, dancing, games – anything of this sort may occupy the first part of the evening, and supper part, with singing, may fit in with the gathering dusk. If music is a difficulty, plan beforehand to have a competent harmonica player or guitarist with you.

WOOL GATHERING

This can fill in a half-hour at a club-in-the-country occasion. Several teams compete, each being allotted a colour and having to collect bits of wool which have been strewn across a field or stretch of open country. The preparation, of course, must be made beforehand, and you must decide then how many teams you are to have. Suppose you settle on four. You might then get four skeins of cheap wool – red, blue, yellow, white, and cut these up into lengths of about nine inches. Twenty-five pieces of each colour will be a convenient number. Now settle an approximately quarter-mile course between two fixed points, perhaps a tree and gate, and strew the bits of wool along it – be sure to scatter the bits singly.

Then assemble your teams; explain which colours they are to collect – warning them to touch none but their own pieces; tell them the starting point and finish of the course, and let them begin their wool gathering. In twenty minutes or so they must be back, with task completed – and the winning team is the one which has collected most.

DOCUMENTARY

This is a project which can occupy one or more outdoor club sessions, and a later indoor one. The idea is for a group of members to visit a village, or a spot notable for its beauty or historical interest, or some sort of building or development work; to prepare a description of it on the spot, and to produce this description in some 'documentary' fashion at the later club meeting. Six to ten is an ideal number for the working team. If a large number of your members are to be occupied simultaneously they can be working on several schemes. One might visit a new road construction; a second, a village; a third, a river or canal lock; a fourth, a sea cove.

Each team will have its leader, and will work out a general plan before starting work. One member might be photographer, another make sketches, a third be responsible for interviewing people with an eye to anecdotes and human interest, still another may get factual detail. Then, of course, there will be the matter of writing and editing the material obtained, and producing it in vivid and interesting form. When the indoor night comes each team might be allowed fifteen minutes to put on its documentary.

An alternative method is to have the whole club let loose on a single project – perhaps visiting a village for an afternoon and evening. Members can then be allotted particular sections for which they are to be responsible – old houses, church, churchyard, local customs and names, reminiscences of local people particularly old inhabitants, impact of modern life on the district, and so on. The collated material can finally make a full evening programme – which will be all the more interesting if the members have kept the result of their researches to themselves and consulted only the Producer.

In any outdoor project of this sort be sure that club members behave with courtesy and consideration in their approaches to the people who help them.

LITTER BLITZ

Keeping the countryside, roads, streets, free of litter is becoming a growing problem. Youth can do so much to solve it. It is good if your young people are frequently warned against being litter-louts, but they are likely to learn much more effectively if they themselves take an active part in keeping the neighbourhood clean. Why not organize a lively 'litter-blitz' – a campaign publicly dramatising the matter, and maybe resulting in a permanent and constructive new attitude towards the problem.

Consultation with Local Authorities and Police should certainly come in at some stage, but to begin you should have full discussion in the club, inviting ideas and hammering out a plan. You might decide to start by a sort of crusade lasting perhaps a week in the district immediately around your club premises, or in some other agreed area. The aim will be not to grumble at or complain about the litter dropped by other people, but to pick it up. The party might go round with truck, buckets, sacks, headed by a banner: 'We are helping to keep Britain tidy.' Ensure that the campaign gets publicity – the local press will gladly co-operate here! The use of additional posters, arm-bands, badges, fancy dress, all such things can best be decided in reference to local circumstances.

And, of course, look inwards as well as outwards, being quite sure that the principles you are advocating apply most plainly in your own club premises.

CLUE HUNT

This is a form of *Treasure Hunt*. A good deal of preliminary work by the leader is involved. First secure the co-operation of five or six people known to your club members and living at convenient distances. With each of these friends you will leave slips of paper, as many slips as you have teams. On each slip is the heading 'Next Clue', then the number of a house (but no street name), then a rhymed couplet which when solved gives the name of the person living in that house, and finally three or four jumbled letters which teams must collect in order to unravel the jumbled sentence at the end of the hunt.

Begin at club headquarters by getting teams of four to six. The leader of each team will carry an authorisation, 'Please give this Team Leader a Clue Slip' which he will produce at each house visited. At the outset you might give to each team a slip with the following: 'No. 16. It could be he blows bellows, or perhaps makes horses' shoes; His house is not called Chestnut – no, another tree he'll choose. – N.E.C.' The teams go into huddles. When they discover the solution they dash to Mr Smith, Lime Tree House, which is number 16 in a not too distant street. Mr Smith, like the teams, has been instructed to hand a slip to a Leader only if he has the other team members with him – this prevents a 'clever one' dashing round on a bicycle without his team members co-operating. Quickly the team gets away from number 16, so that the following rivals may not be guided to it, and set about solving the 'Next Clue' which Mr Smith has given them. It might read: 'No. 33. Perhaps he is a Welshman, perhaps he is a Scot, he plays quite screechy music and marches quite a lot – S.B.F.' This could lead to the home of Mr Piper, living at number 33 in another road. Mr Piper, in turn could hand out a slip leading to Mr Winterbone: 'It isn't Spring or Summer – there isn't any heat (first part of name); It's left behind in butcher's shop when someone's had the meat (second part of name) – N.A.L.' So the hunt goes on through perhaps three other streets. The final clue should read 'Return to hall with all your letters and un-jumble them into four words which are about our Club.' The solution might be 'West Club has fun' and first team to get it wins.

SUMMER HOCKEY

It is fairly easy in summer time to borrow hockey sticks from a school or sports organisation, so why not do this and fix a 'summer hockey' evening for your club. The main difference from the standard game is that you will use one of those large plastic balls, football size. Rounders posts can serve for goals. Mixed teams of course. Play by ordin-ary hockey rules, as far as is convenient. Your members will have tremendous fun.

THERE AND BACK

One person at a time competes, starting from a marked spot at the centre of a fairly large clear space. The person is blindfolded throughout. He travels a certain distance away from his starting point, following certain directions which you give him – and then tries to return unaided, except by his own judgement and memory. The winner is the boy or girl who gets back most nearly to the starting point.

Here are the sort of directions which might be given: 4 paces forward; make half of a right-angle turn to the right; 3 paces forward; make half of a right-angle turn to the left; 4 paces forward; return to starting point.

The 'half of a right-angle turn' is much more difficult

than a simple 'turn right' or left. You may like to vary your instructions for each competitor, but it is actually not easy to get new combinations while retaining the same degree of difficulty. Besides the problem is not in merely remembering what course you have taken but in exactly reversing the turns and measuring out the same steps on your return journey.

It is a good plan for you to move to some different point for each spoken direction, so that the competitor does not take his bearings from you as a fixed point. Also, be prepared to call 'stop' if there is danger of the competitor colliding with something. A stopped person is considered as having failed in his attempt.

CYCLE RALLY

This is most suitable for a rural district with safe cycling on country roads. The programme as given here should occupy about two hours, but a good deal of preliminary preparation is needed. Your first job is to plan the route, and the clues. Allow a total cycling distance of about 12 miles, and not more than 30 clues. Start from club premises, and finish there – so that there can be every convenience in reckoning scores, and refreshments at the end. Competitors should go in pairs, carrying their duplicated sheets of instructions with them. They will write down the solution or required information after each clue.

Here, with fictitious road references, is a sample 'route and clue sheet' which you may adapt to your local requirements:

Out of the door and turn left – **1.** A date above a gate (here follows a space sufficient to write in the answer); **2.** Sunday

69

posting time. *Turn left at road end* – **3.** Telephone number of doctor; **4.** The tallest tree – what is it? *Fork left* – **5.** What is the fare to London? (This could be at a railway notice or bus halt). *Turn right through the alley* – **6.** The price of a hair-cut; **7.** Change where for where. (Could be information about a bus or train.) *Left, and first right* – **8.** What's going free at No. 29? (Could be special offer in grocery store); **9.** Stumps could well be drawn here. (Could be 'close of play' time – of film or theatre show); **10.** Headless alas, and one stands by and weeps. (A broken garden figure, with weeping willow tree). *Over the bridge and right* – **11.** Standing cross centre, giving compass bearing on willow. ('Cross centre' is a cross-roads); **12.** The gate has a name. *Left at the cross-roads and straight on* – **13.** How high is the table for the morning drink? (A stand for milk churns); **14.** Where did they hurt their feet? (A signpost shows the name 'Stonyford'); **15.** . . . . Property of the . . . ('This building is the . . . County Council'); **16.** What is white when it's green? (Greenhouse); **17.** . . . . and not a drop to drink – where are you? (In a loop of the river, by a notice 'this stream is contaminated'). *Turn right on to B1079* – **18.** Who was so kind as to let you rest? (Could be a donor tablet on roadside seat); **19.** When did the clock stop? (The church clock obviously stuck); **20.** Why do tall stories begin here? (There is fishing tackle in the shop window); **21.** Who swung in 1790 and still swings. (An inn sign tells of executed highwayman); **22.** No courting couples here at 11 or 6 on Sunday. (A lych gate – people pass through to church at these times.) *Mount bikes and towards home on B1041* – **23.** The driest place on the road, but what goes on overhead? (Trains over bridge); **24.** Wet this time, and what goes on under there? (A brook); **25.** 12, 21, 9, 7, 14, 5 – where? (On a signpost.) *Over the cross-roads and right* – **26.** Worth searching in year 5,000, but not now. (A refuse tip); **27.** To fetch a pail of water. Name please. (Could be 'Black Hill'). *Left on to B1214* – **28.** Doric or what? (A bank portico.) *Circle the merry-go-round and so to town* – **29.** Could have a blue light, but hasn't. (Police Station); **30.** It's on your own doorstep. (A chalk mark at the club entrance).

A second instruction sheet should be given to each pair. It might run: **1.** This is not a race; cycle carefully; **2.** Don't give away clues; **3.** Follow directions and answer each clue; **4.** Collect 'treasures' as you go (*a*. A piece of haw-thorn, *b*. sheep's wool from hedge or fence, *c*. new postage stamp, *d*. milk bottle top, *e*. freshly-picked nut, *f*, call it Esor and let your nose decide). **5.** Time limit 1 hr 45 mins – there will be a penalty of 1 point for each minute beyond this. **6.** On your return report immediately to club leader who will record your time and give you the general knowledge questions. These could be: Who is Chancellor of the Exchequer; Explain 'Treasure f' reference. ('A rose by any other name . . .'); Where is a near oak tree. **7.** Scores will be as follows: *Clues*, 1 point each; *Treasures*, 5 points each; *General Knowledge questions*, 3 points each.

Finally: Have spaces on the second sheet for filling in *names, times of departure, time of arrival, total time taken, score*. And at the outset start your competitors off at intervals of 1 to 5 minutes – according to number taking part.

CYCLE TREASURE HUNT

This is a variant of the preceding feature, needing similar

preparations. Two organisers can best do it, cycling round the proposed route themselves, in order to work out times and details. The route should be approximately 10 miles, for which 1½ hours can be allowed. Typed or duplicated sheets will be needed, one for each competitor – members can go singly, or in pairs or even threes. A sample sheet is here given, which gives sufficient indication of the sort of thing required:

Cycle Treasure Hunt

Name of Entrants   ..   ..

Time of Departure   ..   ..

Time of Return   ..   ..   ..

(Time allowed 1½ hours. One mark will be deducted for every five minutes beyond the allowance.)

To begin. Turn right on leaving hall. Fork left. Turn right, then immediate left. Proceed for about ¾ mile.

1. Note down here number on keystone of bridge . . . (1 mark). Carry on up road to village.

2. Name which is part bird, part water . . . (2 marks). Turn right at crossroads.

3. Number in red box . . . (1 mark). Proceed until you reach A.41. Turn left. Proceed 100 yards; turn right.

4. How old is stone lodge? . . . (2 marks). Carry on to water.

5. Where does the water come from? . . . (3 marks). Continue to crossroads.

6. Two villages to the right . . . (2 marks). Go straight over to house cluster and visit church.

7. Complete. 'Whosoever thou art that enterest this church' . . . (2 marks). Straight on.

8. How many churches in village? . . . (5 marks).

9. What does monument commemorate? . . . (3 marks).

10. Girl's name on monument . . . (2 marks).

11. Wooden animal nearby . . . (3 marks). Round bend and stop.

12. Name part behind sign-post . . . (5 marks).

13. Song title has sign-post name in . . . (10 marks). Turn left.

14. Number in telephone box . . . (1 mark).

15. Geometrical shape under chestnut tree . . . (2 marks).

16. What time is mail collected? . . . (2 marks). Back to chestnut tree and fork right; pass poplar cluster.

17. What birds live here? . . . (2 marks). Cross A.41. Turn left.

18. Name herd of cows . . . (7 marks). Bear right.

19. Name club member's house . . . (2 marks).

20. The shop open until 10 p.m. . . . (4 marks).

21. Bring in the following: 1945 penny, milk bottle top, dandelion, 4-inch nail, peppermint (3 marks each).
Total marks scored – . . .

At the outset, competitors will be started off at minute intervals.

NIGHT DUTY

Just once in a while let your club members stay up all

night – you may have to choose Friday evening, so that they can catch up on sleep next day.

In the large modern town or city, and even in some country districts, many sorts of people are 'on night duty', working to keep the amenities of ordinary life running smoothly. Let your young people see something of this almost unsuspected activity.

First – perhaps with a small sub-committee of the club – you must investigate the possibilities of your neighbourhood, and make enquiries as to where and how a visit of your young people would be practicable. Then arrange a time-table and itinerary. Supposing you meet at 11 p.m. and finish at 3 a.m., then meals and transport may come into your planning. It may be a good idea to have a supper before you start, a snack part way through, and a warm drink at the end.

The details of your expedition will depend of course on the character of your locality. But here are the sort of items which may be listed for your tour:

Bus depot – cleaners and maintenance men are usually at work from about 10 p.m. to 6 a.m.; *Railway* – signalmen and all sorts of other workers, depending on the size and importance of the station; *Fishermen* – in a typical coastal place the boats come in from around midnight, and unload in readiness for the fish market which may open at 8 a.m.; *All-night garage* – a skeleton staff probably deals with infrequent customers, as well as being ready for breakdown service, and filling in time with repairs; *Watchmen* – whose job it is to patrol factories and large business premises; *Hospital* – night staffs are always working; *Power stations* – generators and so on must run through the night to prepare against the needs of the day; *Gas-works* – similarly, gas-holders nearly depleted must be refilled; *Police station* – just as alive and highly organized as during the hours of light; *Street cleaners* – city streets, often, can only be washed, cleaned, swept during the night; *Road repairs* – when traffic is at the minimum, at night, these too can most easily be effected; *Camps and depots* – military and similar establishments have guards on duty all round the clock; *All-night cafés* – these are often busy where much night work takes place; night-travelling lorry-drivers may be a special class of customer; *Newspaper office* – for a daily paper reporters and editors may be providing and pre-paring news up to 3 or 4 a.m.; printers may be arriving at any time of the night; *Doctors, Veterinary Surgeons, Mid-wives* – all such people are on call throughout the night; *Fire station* – this must be equally prepared at any time.

SPENDING SPREE

Be careful not to let anybody know beforehand what your title means, for the first requirement is that your members shall be divided up into boy-girl couples, all equipped with pencils and paper. There being no chance to with-draw, you can now tell them what they have to do.

Each couple is to be allowed £200 with which to 'set up house'. With this money available they now get out into the town and search shop windows to decide what they can buy – all must aim similarly to furnish living room, bedroom, kitchen. The job must be done really thoroughly, the aim being of course to get complete furnishing and equipment.

There should be no consultation or sharing of ideas; the

fun lies in each couple exercising their own ingenuity and imagination. It must be assumed that the three-roomed flat is in good order, so that no money is needed for decoration, but floors and walls are quite bare and there is nothing built-in beyond ordinary cupboards.

At the end of perhaps an hour all will re-assemble at the club, and enjoy the refreshment break before the final session. Then let each couple in turn report on how they have spent their £200, giving the items bought and the prices paid. It is helpful if the club leader and his wife, or some other experienced married couple, have taken part with the rest, for they can report last of all and probably add to the enlightenment and practical interest of the evening.

FROM HERE TO THERE

This is a lively outdoor feature, but starting from the club room. It can occupy up to an hour, and be organized on a competitive basis. Competitors may go out singly, but will enjoy choosing their own companions, and the thing will go better if they work in twos or threes. Your own preparation will be made beforehand. The task with which they are challenged is to go from *here* to *there* – they will not be told where either place is, but must make their own deductions from the route which is given them.

To begin assemble the competitors and let them copy down on slips of paper the route which you will read from your prepared script. It might run as follows:

'Stand with your back to a church entrance. Walk a short distance to the right until you come to a T junction. Turn left and continue – counting the number of trees on your right – until you reach another T junction. Note down the name painted under the picture which will be visible at this point. Turn right; cross the road, and continue to walk on the left ignoring all turns, until you see a telegraph pole on the right by which is a house name beginning with L. There are two other house names also beginning with L within 50 yards of this. Write down three letters which are common to all three names. Then come back to club room as quickly as possible.'

Of course the foregoing start could only be used if several churches posed the problem of which fitted the instructions. You might just as easily begin: 'Leaving the telephone kiosk on your left, walk straight on', or 'Face the house with the green gable, and cross the street', or 'Leaving the tallest chestnut tree behind you go through the gap in the hedge'. Warn the competitors to think well before they set out, and not to talk loudly or give any other sort of lead to their rivals. You can give a 'free canteen voucher' to the winners, or merely award merit points.

A second way of starting off, which will immediately scatter your competitors, can be used providing a fair number of telephone kiosks are within easy reach. You then announce that the route they have copied down begins at the kiosk with a certain number – and they immediately dash off to find that particular number.

Still another way of starting is to give them a place name jumbled which will be the *here* at the beginning of the route. For instance: U, R, T, Q, M, E, K, R, E, A, S, A (Market Square).

WINDOW SPOTTING

Members are sent out in small groups, each with an agreed

leader, to look at several shop windows – three or four. About 15 minutes may be needed for the actual window inspection. Then all return to the club, settle separately in their groups, and try to answer questions which you put to them. For example: 'What piece of furniture was in the back, left-hand corner', 'In the ironmonger's, what was next to the hammer', 'What colour were the gloves in the drapery window', 'What prices were the tea and coffee?'

The group leaders should write down their answers after consulting their members. Obviously you will need to inspect the windows and list your queries beforehand.

YO-YO

The vogue of the yo-yo returns periodically. It is good to exploit it while the interest lasts, and young club members with a little encouragement can become both enthusiastic and skilful. They themselves may start the vogue!

The basic technique is not difficult to achieve – you merely let the yo-yo run down on its string, and give a smooth but strong upward pull before it has quite reached the bottom, so that there is no pause as it begins the return climb. When this smooth change is really mastered the direction of the descent may be varied, becoming less and less perpendicular. A really skilled exponent can send the yo-yo horizontally and recover it without pause; similarly he can check the descent, and reverse the yo-yo spin at any point on its outward journey. With this stage of ability reached you can experiment with and evolve such competitions as upsetting a skittle, passing the yo-yo through a ring, making it travel towards each wall of the room in turn, as you make four quarter-turns of your body.

Special Events

Guest Evening for
  Older Friends
Coffee Evening
Pre-Nineteenth Century
  Exhibition
Alphabet Museum
Outdoor Games, Indoors
Fine Art Exhibition

Music Appreciation
The Club Entertainment
Starlets Concert
Indoor Games
  Competition
Initiative Test
A Swimming Gala

The items here described are more than half-hour features or mere parts of ordinary club programmes. They are bigger scale things which can well be highspots in the club year.

GUEST EVENING FOR OLDER FRIENDS

This needs careful planning, and some rehearsal for your principal club members.

'Grandparents and Older Friends' roughly describes those who are to be invited. Send out – preferably by hand – formal printed invitation cards (which cost twopence or threepence each), so that you know beforehand how many old folk will be coming. Get three or four mothers, if desired, to undertake making tea or coffee. Club members can make cakes and pastries. All duties must be apportioned well in advance. Be sure that club members arrive a quarter of an hour before the guests. And so, unless they have special duties, are in their seats by opening time. Two rows of chairs should be along the side of each wall – the back row for guests, the front row for club members. On arrival an *Usher* sees that each guest disposes of coat and hat if necessary, then passes him or her to the *Announcer*. The Announcer, who has a loud, clear voice, stands at the hall entrance and calls out the name of the guest for all inside to hear. As the guest steps through he or she is welcomed with handshake and a word of greeting by the *Host* – a senior boy. By his side stands the *Hostess* – a senior girl, who similarly shakes hands and smiles. Then a *Steward* – boy or girl – escorts the guest to a seat. *Stewards* must see that guests are equally divided on the two sides of the hall, for convenience in later competitive events. During the whole of the reception, soft music can be played from a record, or provided by a band of club members. At its conclusion the Chairman of Members' Committee makes a brief speech of welcome to the guests. Then the programme for the evening begins – as described here the whole thing can go through in an hour and a half.

Nursery rhymes contest, a singing game in which the competing teams follow on in singing fresh rhymes, with alphabet chorus in between, until one side fails. There must be a team leader from each side, collecting suggestions from guests and young people and keeping things going.

Attention Twins. This popular game will have club members as the active ones in each team. If desired the boys and girls can be divided into two sets for each side, as shown:

Guest						G
G	1 1			1 1		G
G	2 2	numbered		2 2		G
G	3 3	team		3 3		G
G	4 4	members		4 4		G
G	5 5			5 5		G
G	6 6			6 6		G
G		Leader				G

Scores for each item can then be awarded, 4, 3, 2, 1 for each item. The Leader calls the orders – perhaps: 'Number 3, bring me something square,' and the *threes* dash to their row of guests, and collect what they can – a handkerchief might serve – and carry it to the leader. The important thing is to involve the guests in as many orders as possible, without making them move from their seats. Other orders might be: Shake hands with all your guests; Get their autographs; Give them each a penny – collected from your team; Collect the pennies back.

Solo Items, musical or otherwise can be put in at this point. Then can follow a couple of *dances* – Gay Gordons and Barn Dance are ideal. A few of the guests may join in.

After this, *refreshments*, with smiling girls as waitresses. The club *Ritual* or *Orison* can come next, followed by the last item of the programme, a short *Quiz Contest*, with six guests competing against six club members. In this, as in *Attention Twins*, keep the rivalry keen by frequently announcing the scores.

Finally, *Auld Lang Syne*, and a *Goodnight Circle*, turning in on itself behind a leader so that everybody shakes hands with everyone else – with a few flowers for each lady guest as she departs if you can manage it.

COFFEE EVENING

If you can find a friendly housewife prepared to go to the trouble and expense (total cost may be around £1), your club may have a very pleasant and novel evening out. Her front door should be left open so that members can come and go as they like between say 7 and 9 p.m. A notice 'Coffee House' may be slung on the front gate. In the lounge a record player may be running all the time. Small tables can be spread about with sugar – lump and demerara – and bowls of crisps. Your young folk then strllo in and sit at ease. In the kitchen the housewife, assisted by one or two girls, prepares the coffee and sends it through with plates of sweet biscuits, savouries, open sandwiches, home-made small cakes. The girls will see that no-one has more than a fair share. The food needs to be prepared beforehand, but there is no need to organize anything else, beyond providing coffee. Costs, assuming you are catering for twenty to thirty, may be something like this: tin of coffee 3s.; long bread roll 1s.; ¼ lb. chopped ham 2s. 3d.; sweet biscuits 1s. 5d.; cheese biscuits 1s.; 1 lb. tomatoes 2s. 6d.; sugar 2s.; milk, 4 pints 3s. 0d.; butter 1s.; crisps 1s. 4d.; sliced eggs 1s.; cakes 3s.

PRE-NINETEENTH CENTURY EXHIBITION

This needs perhaps a couple of weeks to prepare. So, choose your teams; warn them that the exhibition is to be in two weeks' time; explain what has to be done, and let them get busy. The idea is for them to search your locality for things belonging to any period before the year 1800 and to mount an exhibition to illustrate as widely as possible such local links.

Actual objects, of course, can form an interesting section – a family Bible, a candle snuffer, an old coin, a fragment of pottery, an old print. Buildings, and remains of buildings, will naturally be important – drawings, plans and photographs of these can be made. Brass rubbings from a church and inscriptions copied from tombstones offer plenty of scope. Trees, streams, bridges, scenic views may be explored. It may be possible to examine old civic and other records, quoting quaint extracts. Anyhow – your teams get all the material they can during their week or two of preparation.

Then, on the night of the exhibition, each has all its finds laid out to the best advantage – if each can use a separate room, so that no ideas can be copied, so much the better. Finally, everybody collects round each exhibition in turn, while a chosen representative gives a brief lecture on his team's display.

ALPHABET MUSEUM

This can be a most intriguing full evening feature:

Split your members into two or more teams – ten in a team makes a useful number. Let no-one know any real details of what is required until the very last minute – it is good, in fact, to announce the whole thing previously as a 'Mystery Evening'. Even when you are giving instructions preface these by the one over-riding rule: 'Anything moved or taken must be afterwards replaced by the same person!'

You can spin some yarn to introduce the thing, and set the right flippant tone, by saying that the club has been asked to compile the beginning of a new local museum, and as it is a task of such importance you are suggesting that the teams each tackle the task independently. Afterwards, you hope the Curator of the British Museum, or someone else, may arrive to judge the exhibitions.

Then allot a separate room, if possible, to each team, and warn them to admit no intruders, so that rivals have no clue as to what each is doing. The object is to produce an exhibit beginning with each letter of the alphabet, and to display the whole lot in artistic, interesting, educational fashion! Allow perhaps half-an-hour for this work. Each team will settle someone to be in charge, and teams will immediately scatter to find exhibits. You should give a little guidance by suggesting that some lucky searcher might find Cinderella's lost slipper, or a stub of pencil used by King John in signing Magna Carta. This labelling of exhibits will have much to do with the success of each museum. For instance an old apple core might be proudly displayed as: A – all that is left of the apple of William Tell's son; (a button) B – burst from the jacket of the world's fattest man in 1891; (a broken chair) C – used by King Canute, and broken as he hurried out of the water; (a diary) D – diary of the Club Leader, when he was a boy in B.C. 23; (a stone) S – believed to have been thrown at invading English by ninth century Welshman.

All team members, of course, will have brought in their treasures in greatest secrecy. When time is called, the Distinguished Adjudicator enters the first room, and both teams gather respectfully round. The Head of the team then explains each exhibit, reading the attached descriptions. The adjudicator awards 3 points for each letter of the alphabet covered; 1 to 3 points for each description; and a maximum of 10 points for the general quality of display. Then he moves into the next room, and repeats. It can easily happen that one team may have everything following on in slick alphabetical order – a considerable display advantage, while the others may not have thought of this. Finally the adjudicator makes his comments and announces the result.

And everyone returns the objects to their original places!

OUTDOOR GAMES, INDOORS

A bustling games session, lasting perhaps an hour, can be had by following on three team games which really belong outdoors but can be very successfully adapted for indoors in a moderately large room.

Indoor Netball. This is simply netball as nearly as your circumstances will allow. Instead of the pole and net each team has one player standing on a chair at the far end of the 'field'. It is his job to hold his arms out in front of him, with fingers clasped, so that they form the equivalent of the netball ring through which the ball must drop. He, of course, can move, providing he stays on the chair, but the ball must drop through his 'arm ring' from the top side. Modifications of ordinary rules can be made on the spot, according to any limiting conditions.

Ring Stick. This is basically like the preceding, except that instead of a ball a tenikoit or rubber ring is used, and the player on the chair instead of looping his arms holds a stick on which he tries to catch the ring. The sticks should be smooth and blunt-ended. Half a broom-handle, with rounded end, is ideal. A team consists of six to ten players. One hand only must be used for catching and throwing – penalty for infringement of this rule, a free throw. No player may take more than two steps while holding the ring, or retain it for more than three seconds – penalty, free throw. Interception is allowed, but not tackling – penalty, an unintercepted penalty throw direct to the Ringer (the person on the chair).

Non-stop Cricket. This is played precisely as outdoors, except that a different ball is used. The ball must not travel far however hard it may be hit, so it should be a hollow plastic skeleton, or of foam rubber, plain sponge, wool.

FINE ART EXHIBITION

This is a stunt exhibition which can form the main feature of an 'open club evening', or be a special feature by itself perhaps on a Saturday afternoon. Considerable space is needed, maybe a hall and several rooms, and a good deal of preparation is involved. The exhibits must be arranged in sections; very clearly labelled and numbered, and not unduly crowded – some can be fastened to walls, some spaced on tables. A *Guide to the Exhibition* should be on sale to every person entering; duplicated sheets can easily be managed. At the entrance to each room or section a large-lettered title should be displayed.

Here is an outline for the full exhibition, under its sectional headings, with the titles which will appear in the *Catalogue* or *Guide*, together with the actual articles on display bracketed after the titles.

Portraits. **1.** A popular Singer (kettle); **2.** Sweet Seventeen (seventeen lumps of sugar); **3.** Companions of the Bath (soap and flannel); **4.** The Woodcutter (axe); **5.** A Holy Friar (frying pan with holes in bottom); **6.** The Father of Knox (hammer); **7.** A Poor Retainer (colander); **8.** His Majesty in Oils (coin in oil); **9.** A Reigning Favourite (umbrella); **10.** A Sharp Customer (razor blade).

Land and Sea Scenes. **11.** The Black Sea (black-painted C); **12.** A Modern Clipper (hair clip); **13.** A Well-known Prison (cage, mousetrap); **14.** View of Blackpool (ink in saucer); **15.** Wreck of the Cutter (old knife); **16.** Washed Ashore (clean washing); **17.** A Swimming Match (floating matchstick); **18.** Off the Needles (knitting, off the needles); **19.** All Hands Lost (watch or clock without hands).

Naval and Military. **20.** The Charge of the Light Brigade (electric light bill); **21.** Hero of Many a Scrape (old grater); **22.** Mustered for Inspection (tin of mustard); **23.** 'A' Battery (torch battery); **24.** Boers in the Wood (block of wood with holes); **25.** The Guard (fireguard); **26.** The Silent Navy (toy lead seaman); **27.** Result of the War with China (broken china).

Country Subjects. **28.** The Deserted Home (birds' nest); **29.** The Water Otter (gas ring or kettle); **30.** Nothing but Leaves (lettuce); **31.** The Lay of the Last Minstrel (egg); **32.** Anything to Grind? (false teeth); **33.** Outside the Wood (tree bark); **34.** A Hunting We Will Go (small toothcomb); **35.** A Group of Yews (several U's on piece of paper); **36.** The Lynx in Repose (cuff links); **37.** The Sower of Tares (needle); **38.** Spring is Here (small spring).

Aviation. 39. B.O.A.C. (button, oil, apple, coin); **40.** Master of the Air (bicycle pump); **41.** Pan-AM Airways (pan, ham, comb and hair roller); **42.** Undercarriage Up (toy cart or motor lying on its back); **43.** A View of Space (exercise-book page headed Composition); **44.** B.E.A. (berry, eraser, ash); **45.** Roger, and Out (a letter: 'Dear Roger – I'm through with you – Janet.')

Miscellaneous. 46. Stop Her! (stopper); **47.** Hot Jazz (Jazz written in red on hot-water bottle); **48.** A Friend in Need (safety pin); **49.** Clasped Together (snap fasteners); **50.** Five Acres and a Cow (five old teeth and a lead cow); **51.** Top of the Pops (bottle tops); **52.** An Off-hand Affair (glove); **53.** The Old Organ-blower (handkerchief); **54.** The Seasons (cruet); **55.** A Stirring Subject (spoon); **56.** Capital of Scotland (S); **57.** Off the Cliffs of Dover (chalk); **58.** The Tongue that Never Lied (shoe tongue); **59.** A Study in Reflections (a small pocket mirror); **60.** The Watch on the Rhine (a watch and bacon rind); **61.** An Absorbing Subject (sponge); **62.** Off the Line (washing); **63.** The Overthrow of Greece (candle with grease down its side, fallen over); **64.** A Patched Peace (patched piece of clothing); **65.** The Results of a Blow (inflated balloon); **66.** Stabbed to the Heart (cabbage with a knife in it); **67.** The Waits (some weights); **68.** Mightier than the Sword (pen); **69.** More than a match (several matchsticks); **70.** Not Taken Yet (medicine); **71.** We Part to Meet Again (open scissors); **72.** Relics of the Great (cinders); **73.** After Tea (U).

Special. 74. The Masterpiece (large mirror on stand, covered over, the cover to be lifted by viewer).

MUSIC APPRECIATION

When a suitable concert is to happen in your locality plan to take your club members, but get in some worthwhile preparation beforehand.

Supposing it is a Chopin recital, then plan a talk, or study group, or preliminary playing linked with Chopin, so that your members get a knowledgeable background and some acquaintance with 'the man and his music' beforehand. The concert will then be much more enjoyable. And you may be able to have an interesting discussion afterwards.

THE CLUB ENTERTAINMENT

General Hints. If a stage entertainment is to go smoothly many people must co-operate. In addition to the folk at the door who admit the audience and the stewards who show them to their seats, you probably need such specialists as Compère or Chairman, Pianist or Conductor, Lighting man, Stage Managers or Scene-shifters, Make-up people. You may even want a Photographer who takes pictures while the show is on, or somewhere backstage before or after items.

Such responsible people should each be provided with a special, appropriate programme. The same general programme will be the basis for all, but particular details will need to be added. *Compère* – any introductory comments, or information about cast and producer; *Pianist* – details of required accompaniments; *Lighting man* – special effects, colourings, blackouts, and so on; *Stage Managers* – exact list of properties needed for each part of the show; *Make-up people* – details of characters needed, and approximate times by which they must be ready; *Photographer* – precise moments at which pictures can most satisfactorily be taken.

Take care to consult the Police or Local Authorities if you are in any doubt about regulations applying to your entertainment. Is a Theatrical Licence necessary? Are your exits, gangways, general fire precautions adequate? Is there independent lighting over exit doors? Do you have a hatchet, blanket, extinguisher backstage, and do your curtains need to be fireproofed? Should the chairs be fastened together? Do you need to pay entertainment tax and to claim refund, or do you use programmes sold at the requisite prices, which ensure seats – without guaranteeing that a person not having a programme can therefore be refused permission to enter? Does any of the music you propose to use involve permission by the Performing Rights Society?

Showmanship. So many entertainments, good in their separate items, prove dull and tedious when they are put on, simply because they lack polish, slickness, efficiency, effective presentation – all the things which may be summarized as 'showmanship'.

Your club entertainers should develop this quality in all their performances. The gaining of it can be a most profitable and interesting 'activity', whose aim might be defined as preventing an audience ever saying after a show, 'What they needed was a little more life'.

Unless you put 'pep' into any programme it is likely to flop, no matter how note- and word-perfect the folk on the stage may be. In a programme of varied items this is particularly necessary. There must be variety in the items, for monotony and sameness are deadly.

Stage-manage your performance well. Plan the 'curtains', and see that they work slickly. If the curtain must remain down for any length of time, fit one or two stunts in front of it. See that every performer can make a good bow and give a cheery smile. Don't have a moment wasted between items, and avoid all noise behind the curtain. Begin strongly and punctually, and end with a snap – both the whole show and each single item.

If a choir or band is on the stage, it should be warned against inattention during solo items – there should be no shuffling or whispering. If the members look and listen appreciatively when solo performers are taking their turns the audience will do the same. Everyone should look happy – an audience reacts strongly to the emotions expressed by those on the stage, so grimaces and grimness should be guarded against.

The leader or compère should be alert, brisk, cheerful, debonair. His finger should be on the pulse of the audience, and if necessary he should improvise programme changes to get them warmed up. But, though he may experiment with discretion, those giving the show must always be aware of whatever changes are being made.

It is generally preferable not to announce items. It usually pays the leader better to smile at the audience than to talk much to them. And if they have printed programmes then spoken announcements are superfluous.

Should the names of people in the show need to be spoken it is always better to give Christian names than to say Mr or Miss.

Lighting is important. Different colour effects brighten a show very considerably, and you will almost certainly be able to find some member of the club, or a friend, who likes tinkering with electrical gadgets and so will be delighted at the chance of showing what he can do for your stage. Curtains and background are equally important. The handicraft sections of the club, and the potential artists, have plenty of scope here. Your aim must be to provide an attractive view for the audience both when the curtain is up and when it is down.

The danger periods of a show are those during which the curtain is down – the between-item periods. Good organization will ensure that these are reduced to the minimum, but constant care is necessary to avoid slackness and confusion behind the scenes.

Calypso for Club Show. A calypso is an excellent way of opening a club entertainment, for you can write your own pungent and topical words. Two or three boys, preferably with guitars, and a girl singer can do the whole item, maybe with an occasional background of twisting or jiving teenagers. If your guitar players are not competent then get the actual music taped and let the instrumentalists mime the playing.

It is fairly easy to get calypso music. You may either first select a tune, and then write words to fit it; or you may write your words to taste and then find a tune which fits them.

Here is a sample, which can readily be adapted. It envisages two boys and one girl for the singing, with other girls forming chorus or dancing line behind.

1. *Introducing Youth Club's Annual Show,*
   You'll enjoy each minute till you go,
   Calypso now, let's make up rhyme,
   Guarantee a smashing real fine time

   Chorus

   This is our annual Youth Club show,
   Everyone will have a go,
   Boy, girl, each son and daughter,
   Enjoy fun just like they oughter.

2. *This show tonight is number twenty-one,*
   We guess that it's our town's record run,
   Three or four we have helped to fix,
   But Club Leader's been here since 1066.

3. (Boys) *The girls, don't you think, are rather cute,*
   That one just there is quite a beaut.
   (Girl) *Cut it out, you boys* (To audience) *now*
   listen to me
   And I'll tell you what you're gonna see.

4. (Boys) *Oh come off it, Rosemary, be a pal,*
   They like our voice, they like it well.
   (Girl) *You'll annoy Professor Alley* (or whoever
   is in charge of lighting), *with rage he'll foam,*
   He'll fuse all the lights and we'll have to go home.

5. *The oldest in the audience is ninety-nine,*
   But still he feels so nice and fine,
   At each annual show he'll smile and say,
   It's the boys and girls that keep me gay.

6. *But you'll want to see them now we've warmed the
    stage.*
    (Rosemary) *You like my singing* (Boys) *They're
    wild with rage.*
    (All) *It's a smashing opening, you'll all agree*
    (Rosemary) *Because I'm in it,* (1st boy) *And me,*
    (2nd boy) *And me!*

STARLETS CONCERT

The usual Club Show consists of plays, stunts, songs,
sketches, in all of which a number of folk take part. In
such a programme it is generally advisable not to have
strictly solo items – for you may have three gaps and six
people ready to fill them, with the consequent awkward-
ness of making a choice.

A good solution for this dilemma is to have a special and
different concert or show in which only solo items are
included. This gives opportunity for the boy who has
learned to play the harmonica, the girl who works at the
piano, the ballet student, the keen elocutionist or conjurer.
You will probably be surprised at the number of items it is
possible to get when you begin exploring for 'starlets'. The
amount of publicity you give to the show must depend on
the number, variety, and quality of its features, and your
confidence in them. But at the least you will be able to
depend on the friends and relatives of the artistes to form
an appreciative audience. And you will be equally sure of
giving much encouragement to the young people who,
individually, are making efforts to acquire personal skill
and ability.

INDOOR GAMES COMPETITION

An inter-club games evening should include table-tennis, chess, draughts, darts. In order to get a manageable and balanced programme the number of competitors must be restricted. The actual membership of the competing teams has a bearing on this, but here is a suggested scheme.

Table Tennis (single) – a maximum of four boys and four girls from each club; *Chess* – two players from each; *Draughts* – four players from each; *Darts* – four boys and four girls from each. No competitor should be allowed to take part in more than one game.

INITIATIVE TEST

Two or three boys should attempt this together, starting Friday evening, and getting back before Sunday. The details of the excursion will depend entirely on the type of locality in which it is planned and the relative likelihood of walking as against hitch-hiking. But an average sort of scheme might run as follows:

The boys are allowed perhaps half-a-crown each. They must travel to a point 75 miles away, and return. At the farthest point a free breakfast should be available for them, through the kindness of a local club or church, between the hours of 8.30 and 10.30 a.m. The boys must obtain written evidence that they have reached this farthest point. En route they should have to visit two towns or places of interest and report fully on some particular feature in each – it might be a museum, the way traffic is organized, the notable specimen trees and plants in a botanic garden, the health and organization of youth clubs – signed confirmation from some local person should be evidence that this investigation has been properly done.

Of course they will have small chance to sleep on that Friday night. A full written log should be insisted on. Be sure that they have a telephone number at your 'home base', which however they must not call up except in real emergency. Incidentally in mountainous or open country three boys are better than two, for in case of accident one can stay with the injured person while the third goes for help.

Don't anticipate trouble however, the whole adventure should be tremendous fun and a real test of initiative.

A SWIMMING GALA

General Hints. Swimming galas vary so much. There are those in which thousands of spectators are catered for by programmes starring champions of every sort and in which world-titles are competed for; on the other hand there are homely little affairs where some club decides to have a rollicking afternoon with such varying talent, or lack of it, as may be available.

Supposing that you are secretary, you will need first to get a committee to help you, and together you will appoint officials. If you have enough people they can be: *two judges* – who, standing one at each side of the bath, record the order of finishing of all the competitors in any race, and award points in such things as fancy swimming and diving; *starter* – who, having assured himself that all are ready, gives the starting signal; *timekeeper* – with stop-watch; *announcer* – who calls out events and names; *whip* – whose job it is to see that the programme runs to time. You cannot so well manage with fewer than those, though the last two or even three may be telescoped. It may be possible to add: *check starters* – who see that the competitors start properly; *referee*, whose decision is accepted when judges disagree – for instance, if the first judge has placed the competitors' orders of finishing in a race 6, 1, 4, 2, 3, 5, and the second judge has 6, 4, 1, 2, 3, 5, then the referee's decision, whatever it is, possibly 1, 6, 4, 2, 3, 5, is accepted; the referee also watches that swimmers are not interfered with by opponents; *stewards* – some to supervise competitors, one to look after bath equipment, one to attend to programmes, one to have charge of refreshments, one to take care of the prizes, and perhaps a chief steward to supervise all these others. Then you will have yourself to go on with arrangements for programmes, seating and dressing accommodation, tickets, score sheets, advertisements, bath equipment for special events, and possibly refreshments and music.

While expert knowledge is not absolutely essential for your officials, you certainly must have properly competent people to judge diving or style events.

In a competition for style or diving try to get three judges who award their points independently, allowing a maximum of ten for each item. When the event is finished each judge must total his points and place the competitors in their respective orders – first, second, third. These placings figures of the judges are then added together, and that competitor is the winner whose aggregate is the lowest. Should there be a tie the points of the judges, instead of the placing marks, are added – they are less likely to be the same.

There should be at least one 'star' item in your programme, if it can be managed, for that will have much to do with attracting spectators – it may be a championship race, a demonstration, a polo-match. For the rest, get your programme thoroughly mixed; there is nothing more deadly dull than a long series of plain races. Intersperse humorous events, team races, diving, fancy swimming and life-saving displays, demonstrations of strokes, stunts and contests. Remember, in your planning, that competitors need to be considered; they must not be brought into one event after another without reasonable rest between.

And don't make your gala too long – two hours is always better than three, and an hour-and-a-half generally better than two, providing the time is thoroughly packed with action.

Diving should not take too much of the time; it can easily become boring because it has no competitive thrill like a race.

The Programme. The important thing in planning your items for an open gala is to have something for everybody – girls, boys, swimmers, even non-swimmers. Here is a suggested programme: **1.** One length race, free-style (boys under 13); **2.** One length, free-style (boys 13 and over); **3.** One length, free-style (girls under 13); **4.** One length, free-style (girls 13 and over); **5.** Tug-of-war (teams) – the rope is stretched across the bath, that team winning which pulls its opponents into the water; **6.** Diving (open) – one plunge, header, or other dive to be performed; **7.** One length, back stroke (open); **8.** Hand-in-hand race (teams) – team members stand in cluster or line, holding hands, they jump into shallow water and travel individually in any way way they choose across the pool, or to the bath end, that team winning which first has all its members on the bank and holding hands again; **9.** Style contest (open) – any two strokes to be demonstrated for a few yards by each entrant; **10.** Clothes race (open) – each competitor goes in from the side, crosses the bath, climbs out, dons shirt and trousers (boys) or skirt and blouse (girls), jumps back and swims to the starting side; **11.** Relay race.

The winners of events 1 to 4 can choose teams for event **11.** Points (3, 2, 1) can be awarded the first three in events **1, 2, 3, 4, 6, 7, 9** to determine the 'swimming champion'.

Apart from straightforward races and contests, and demonstrations, there are a wide variety of other possible events.

Races. The following names are self-explanatory – candle race; ball-and-spoon race; balloon races – blowing; obstacle race; three-legged race; barrel race – sitting astride, swimming and pushing, sitting inside and paddling; motor-tyre race – lying across and paddling. In a 'rescue race' two teams compete – a tyre, with rope attached, is thrown to the on-coming swimmer who clambers into it and is hauled to land; the tyre must be thrown beyond a fixed mark. Each team member is 'rescued'.

Contests. Here also the names are sufficient – mop fight, pushball, pillow fight, greasy pole, raft wrestling, raft boxing.

Stunts. Comic processions, comic rescues, clownish combats, all such things can come under this heading. You may have an *over* 90 race – two or three bearded ancients arriving in bath-chairs and competing humorously, you may plan a *boating accident* or have a swimmer pursued by a rubber or wood shark, towed along by a string fastened to his own waist. A *cork scramble* is always good fun – a large number of corks being tossed into the pool and the competing swimmers each trying to secure the biggest number within a given time.

A very popular old stunt is the *Monte Cristo sack feat*. A weighted sack; a performer crouching in it on the edge of the pool; an assistant knotting a rope round the top and pushing his victim into the water – and the victim rising a moment later from the opened mouth of the sack. Everything depends on the rope. It is doubled, and the doubled end passed through a hole into the sack where it is held by the swimmer inside. Thus, although the two ends are tied round the sack and knotted no matter how securely as soon as the one inside releases his doubled end it slips out through the hole and the sack-mouth is free. But try it on land beforehand!

A Demonstration. If you have a few particularly good swimmers you may arrange a demonstration of strokes, or fancy swimming, or methods of learning, or life-saving.

In any of these the water work should so be planned that all spectators have a good view. Someone with a clear voice should stand on the side and give necessary explanations concisely. Suppose you have a swimmer competent to demonstate a variety of swimming strokes. If your bath is not too long he might do a full length by each style, while the one on the bank makes brief comments. Be careful to plan in advance so that the swimmer can easily memorize his programme.

The following is a suggested outline for the announcer's remarks. The procedure is this – the swimmer comes out to the bath end, waits while the announcer reads the first paragraph, then plunges in; having done the first length he stands or grips the rail for a moment's rest while the announcer is reading the second paragraph, then the second length is swum, and so on. Or, of course, you may have a number of different exponents, each demonstrating one stroke.

Announcer's Commentary:

1. *Racing plunge* – followed by *front-crawl stroke* – the fastest method of swimming. Notice how the breath is taken through the mouth at each stroke. Correct breathing is the real secret of crawl, together with co-ordinated action.

2. *Side-stroke* – an easy, comfortable stroke. A very common fault in this is to roll over on to the breast each time the top arm reaches forward.

3. *Overarm* – a graceful development of side-stroke. Practically the only difference is the out-of-water recovery of the top arm. In both these strokes the head should be low.

4. *Sculling* for a few yards. Then a feat that is troublesome in fresh water for most men – *Motionless horizontal-floating*. Though this looks so easy it is much more difficult than anything else that has yet been done. Now the *trudgen stroke* – which you see is a double overarm method, with one scissor-kick to the two arm-drives.

5. *Underarm back-stroke* – an old-fashioned style, but very useful in developing powerful arm-action, and the flat, horizontal position which marks all good swimming.

6. *Back-crawl stroke* – the fastest back-swimming style; notice the graceful relaxation at the arm recoveries.

7. *Life-saving back-stroke* – this, of course, is not fast, but it is very strong, and allows both hands to be used in holding a drowning person. If you want to test the quality of your kick next time you are in the water try holding your arms straight up into the air, like this.

8. *Short-arm or racing breast-stroke* – this illustrates well the rule by which you may judge any swimming – 'the better the swimmer the fewer the strokes'. Notice the mouth breathing, and the way in which energy is saved by the long glides.

9. *Butterfly stroke* – this racing style is a curious combination of leg action rather between that of breast-stroke and crawl, and a breast-stroke arm movement in which the arms recover through the air, thus reducing resistance . . . and that, ladies and gentlemen, concludes the demonstration.

Music and Dancing

Rhythm Band	Write Your Own Hymn
Rhythm Corner	National Features
Songfest	Jiving for Juniors
Club Choir	Polish your Dancing
Club Pop Singers	Jive Session
Carols by Candlelight	Dance Eliminations

Dancing and music so naturally form a prominent part of club life, and here are ways good use can be made of them.

RHYTHM BAND

Ideally you should have a piano and some solo instrument as the basis for your band, but with just a moderately able pianist you still can have plenty of fun. Though you may set out to provide a feature for one evening it is likely that the new musical activity will not stop with the single night.

The 'rhythm instruments' are easily provided: tins containing dried peas – to shake; washboards – to scrape; tins with sticks – as drums; stones – to knock together; pieces of glasspaper – to chafe. You may invent heaps of others!

Seat your players like an orchestra, having each class of 'instruments' grouped together. Then begin rehearsing, taking one group at a time. Practice them with duple and triple rhythms, counting 1, 2; 1, 2, or 1, 2, 3; 1, 2, 3, getting accent always on each 'one'. When the 'instrumentalists' have some idea of the sounds they can make, and how to produce them in unison, you can attempt your first tune. *The Happy Wanderer* can make an excellent start.

As the band becomes proficient you can get tune variations by repeating verses with single groups of instruments, or by humming, or singing in addition.

RHYTHM CORNER

The playing of pop records is a common enough part of the club evening, with members fitting dance steps, or just listening. Just a few however, may like to do something more. That was how skiffle groups originated – folk unable to play real instruments taking as active a part as they could in rhythmic music. So why not have a 'rhythm corner' where drumming and percussion effects can be practised and enjoyed? A real set of drums, of course, would be ideal, but you can have plenty of fun with improvisations – as suggested in the preceding section. You can hit tin trays or boxes with padded sticks or bunched wires, or instead of a metal surface you can have a cardboard carton or just a chair seat. The important thing is not so much the sound effect produced as the rhythm with which it is sounded. So you must know how the desired rhythm fits into the general pattern of the music. There are two ways in which you can get your 'musicians' to study this matter and become proficient. One, by listening to and imitating the way a band performs on a popular record. Two, by analysing the rhythm structure of musical bars and so deciding exactly what is to be 'played' and how.

The first is straight-forward enough. For the second you will need a little musical knowledge, and must impart a little also to your 'students'.

The music you are concerned with is primarily rhythmic, held together by a firm structure of accented bass notes perhaps built up by piano or string bass. Melody is less essential, and can meander freely and irregularly – it has little to do with your rhythm group; their job is supporting the main rhythmic structure. They do this by a sort of secondary off-beat structure of their own, fitting closely together with the basic accented beats and sometimes even overshadowing it. Getting this independent rhythm is their job, and they can develop ability by practising the possibilities in progressively more difficult forms. Begin with straightforward tapping or brushing on every beat in a two- or four-time piece of music. Do the same with three-time. Then take your duple or common time tune and omit the unaccented alternate beat, in a two- or rfou-time piece omitting second and fourth. Follow by getting only the accented first beat of triple time, omitting second and third beats. Next try playing the unaccented instead of the accented portions, drumming only second and fourth in common time or second and third in triple time. The next stage will be mentally to split each beat into two halves, playing only second halves. Thus you imagine each beat in a bar of common time to consist of two quavers, and you rest for each first quaver and play each second. A still more complex form would be to imagine each crotchet value of the common time to consist of a triplet of quavers, the drummer playing the second and third notes of each triplet. He might even play the second and third of one triplet, only the third of the second, and so on in this alternate fashion.

Once these basic rhythms have been mastered your players will be able to improvise on them and vary them at will within any piece of music. Maybe out of all this a club band of your own may one day emerge.

SONGFEST

Songfest is a good American-German name for a singing festival or feast, so can be interpolated excellently into a club evening feature – combining it with a *Barbecue* or *Sausage Sizzle*. There will, of course, be known favourites with your members, and these songs will certainly have their place. But try to get one or two novel items in addition, and make these the high spots of the singsong.

For instance, *Kum Ba Yah* can be a quick favourite almost anywhere. It is a negro spiritual, and the words *Kum Ba Yah* mean simply 'Come by here'.

2. *Someone's crying, Lord, Kum ba yah!*
3. *Someone's singing, Lord, Kum ba yah!*
4. *Someone's praying, Lord, Kum ba yah!*

Daniel, Daniel (Youth Sing Book No. 303) is lively by any standards, when taken by two groups, each responding with their alternate words. It can be made livelier still if each group jumps to its feet to declaim its own word or phrase. The bobbing up and down, incidentally, assists in maintaining a good rhythm. Should your singers be seated on the floor and so unable to get to their feet quickly enough, they may fling their arms above their heads instead.

Still another idea is to write your own Club song, perhaps commemorating a summer camp or some other special event. Make it as descriptive as possible, and introduce plenty of club names. Choose some familiar song as a pattern, so that you can follow its meter and rhymes, and your members will be able to sing it right away. *The Long, Long Trail* makes a good model. One obvious start could be:

> *There's a long, long trail a-winding*
> *Down from our club room to the camp,*
> *Where Camp Warden waits to greet us*
> *As we end our burdened tramp.*
> *In his arms hot water bottles,*
> *Sheets and pillow smooth and soft,*
>   *etc.*

Widdicombe Fair is just as good, for in place of 'Old Uncle Tom Cobleigh and all' you can put a string of club characters.

Another which can usefully be parodied is *The Quartermaster's Stores*. This is particularly useful for introducing people by name, so that each individual in turn can be pilloried. Here are suggestions:

> *1. There is Skip, Skip –has a lot of lip*
> > *In our camp, in our camp;*
> > *There is Skip, Skip –has a lot of lip,*
> > *In our Youth Club's annual camp.*
> Chorus
> *This awful camp is killing me,*
> > *I wish I'd brought my Mum with me,*
> > *I wish I'd brought my Mum with me.*
> *2. There is Dean, Dean, pitch him in the stream.*
> *3. There is Stubb, Stubb – ruins all the grub.*
> *4. There is Smith, Smith –who's the girl he's with?*
> *5. There is Yule, Yule – really quite a . . . jewel.*
> *6. There is Stokes, Stokes – let's get rid of him folks.*
> *7. There is Nick, Nick – beat him with a stick.*

Or the song can be a more general bit of club folklore, really well done so that it will stand up to a lot of wear. New verses can always be added as the traditions grow and new personalities emerge. Make quite an occasion of the launching of such a folksong, giving it a considerable build-up. You can announce the *Première*, when it will be introduced. The verses can be sung solo, and the chorus – which may be written on a black-board – shared by everybody. If you can have duplicated copies for the members so much the better. But be sure to retain the words for future and permanent use. Here is another version, with the club's initials as B.M.S.S.

There is fun, fun, in everything that's done
In our club, in our club
1. *There is fun, fun, in everything that's done*
In our top-pop hi-fi Club

Chorus

A cheerful lot of folk are we
And not one frown you ever see,
And not one frown you ever see.

2. *B.M.S. – S. – gosh how they do dress,*
In our club, in our club
B.M.S. – S. – gosh how they do dress,
In our top-pop hi-fi Club.

Chorus

3. *There's D.P. – gee! – and Alan – handsome he!*
4. *There are girls, girls, full of whirls and curls.*
5. *There are boys, boys, bringing all the joys.*
6. *There's Virginner – ginner – always quite a winner.*
7. *There is Suze, Suze, the one the boys all choose.*
8. *There is Barry, Barry, some poor girl will marry.*
9. *And the rest, rest, they're all the very best.*

If, to round off an evening, you want other songs, get the *Youth Sing Book* and follow with *Home on the Range* (228), *Oh Jemima* (373), *Old Folks at Home* (174), *Green Grow the Rushes-ho* (181), *My Bonnie Lies Over the Ocean* (176), *The Bee* (350), *The Two Brothers* (308), *Frère Jacques* (286), *Goliath of Gath* (360).

CLUB CHOIR

The toughened boys' club leader may be tempted to scoff at the suggestion of part singing as a club activity – till the thought of the popularity of singsongs makes him pause. And obviously, in a mixed club the matter appears quite differently – girls' voices with those of the boys which have not yet begun to change, together with the settled basses and tenors of the older male members, can make very delightful music.

Of course, as in all club music – and any cultural matter – nearly everything will depend on the enthusiasm and ability of the activity leader. Given the right man or woman your club choir can become exceedingly popular and enjoyable.

Christmas probably whetted the appetites of your members, especially if they went out as a club carol party. So remind them of what fun that was, and invite them to have another go, with longer term ambitions. The *Youth Sing Book* has almost limitless material. The more of your members who learn to read music the better. Certainly all should have some elementary knowledge, and the study of this should be part of early practices. Rounds make an interesting and useful beginning.

Let voice production and the proper technique of singing also have place – under the most competent instructor available.

A common fault in singing is to attack a note with the throat partially closed. An open mouth does not necessarily mean an open throat. A hard, set face must be avoided – smiling helps – and if the tongue is depressed and the throat kept loose and free there is full and free passage for the voice.

Breathing is also important, using the diaphragm, so that the chest is filled from the bottom upwards. The proper method is to inhale through the nose, and to expel the air with lips slightly parted. Both consonant and vowel sounds need special attention, together with breath control. If a soft note is sung with a weak backing of breath it will be of poor quality; the lungs should always be kept well filled. Regulate the breathing to the length of the phrase being sung, and keep a sufficient reserve to enable the phrase to finish well.

In scale singing – and individuals as well as full choir should do this – there is a tendency to allow the throat to become tense and closed as the top notes are reached. A relaxed throat and depressed tongue will cure this, and so preserve the tone of quality all through.

The vowel sounds ah, aw, ee, u, oa, oo will each be worked in turn in long and short sounds; then the vowel sounds with consonants, ending each sound with 'ing'. 'T' must be spoken distinctly, and not like 'd'; 'p' must not sound like 'b'.

Naturally your club choir will want to spend much of its time singing songs. But equal care must mark this second side of your practices. The phrasing of words and their meaning should be studied, and necessary breath control noted. So, in turn, articulation, breath control, correct time, expression, will each get attention.

Don't be unduly eager to give public performances until the club choir has become really polished. The best way to start off will be with just single items in the annual concert, and earlier still at 'inside' entertainments of lesser importance. Practice, and plenty of it, must always precede performance.

CLUB POP SINGERS

Most clubs have one or two girls and boys who like imitating their favourite pop singers. Such proclivities are worth encouraging – but there is always difficulty in getting suitable accompanying music. Have you tried letting your singer go along with an actual record, covering up the recorded vocalist? This can work well with selected records in which the singer has breaks during which the accompanying band alone sounds. All you have then to do is to turn down the vocal sections so that your singer is clearly heard, then turn up the band parts so that they make balanced strong sections between, keeping your singer in tune and filling out satisfactorily to match his singing strength. An alert listener with careful hand on the volume control can achieve a fine performance, the band work making your singer feel, and sound, almost as good as his singer model!

CAROLS BY CANDLELIGHT

It really is worth-while to get the candles if at all possible, and to use them alone for lighting, for they give such a warm, friendly, nostalgic atmosphere. But there must be enough light for singers to read words. A little experimenting will determine whether an electric light suitably tinted can be added.

If possible have a good pianist, though other instruments can help if you can get them. You must have sufficient copies of words for all to read, otherwise you are likely to dry up after the first verse or two of the more familiar hymns or songs. There is an extensive carol section in *The Youth Sing Book*, and a 'words only' edition is available. Be sure to sing some of the less well-known carols, like 'Ding Dong! Merrily on High', 'On this day is the Saviour born', 'Masters in this hall'. And try some of the French versions and 'O come all ye faithful' in Latin, or 'Silent Night' in German.

WRITE YOUR OWN HYMN

Decide on a simple shape and metre, perhaps – '*Let us with a gladsome mind, praise the Lord for He is kind*' – then let your young people, singly or in groups, write similar verses which can be sung later. It is helpful to allot subjects. In the following examples, produced by the younger members of a club, the allotted subjects will be plain enough:

> *Praise Him for the pets we own,*
> *They bring happiness to our home.*
> *For all lovely things to eat*
> *We sing praises at Thy feet.*
> *Thank Him for the songs we sing,*
> *Always let our praises ring.*
> *Praise Him for the countryside,*
> *Fields and woodlands far and wide.*
> *Let's thank Him for ships of old,*
> *And for knights and shipmen bold.*
> *Praise Him for the games we play,*
> *Praise Him, praise Him all the day.*
> *Thank you God for summer sun,*
> *Sea and sand and lots of fun.*
> *Praise Him for the ice and snow,*
> *And the winter winds which blow.*
> *Lord we thank Thee for the rose*
> *Which within our garden grows.*

Praise the Lord for all our friends,
All our naughty ways He mends.

You can write the whole thing up on blackboards, so that everyone may sing, or you may have each couplet sung by its proud originators. Use the tune *Monkland*, or if you want to be more modern sing your hymn to the tune *Michael, row the boat ashore*, adding an '*Alleluia*' at the end of each line.

NATIONAL FEATURES

Nowadays there is increasing interchange and contact with young people of differing nations. Some of your own club may be host to teenagers of another nationality. In either case it is good to be prepared with song and dance items which you consider characteristic and which will be novel and interesting to the other folk. So make a choice of even a couple of songs and two dances and polish them to a high standard so that you can perform them adequately, when occasion arises.

Dances? Would *Sir Roger de Coverley* and *Dashing White Sergeant* do? Or are there others which appeal more to you? And for songs – what about *Clementine, Woad, Green grow the rushes-ho*?

But learn them really well, so that you can perform them with assurance and style. You may, of course, prefer items which are characteristic of your own particular part of the country – maybe your own Club Song. Whatever your choice make sure you do it reasonably well.

JIVING FOR JUNIORS

The modern commercialised boosting of dances for teenagers has had some curious results. A good many youth clubs have found 'jive sessions' extremely popular and have encouraged them so much that their members want to do little else. But younger boys and girls, who like to imitate the older ones, have found that they can twist and wriggle as well as their older brothers and sisters, and the teenager has been faced with the awkward fact that in modern dance forms he is often merely doing 'kid's stuff'. The unfortunate thing is that several years' preoccupation with such styles can leave teenagers incapable and un-skilled in other things, and extremely deficient in the social graces which belong to the more adult and all-round social or dance or party. The up-to-date club leader there-fore will do well to begin to rectify this weakness. Young people may sulk if games or less familiar dances are sug-gested at a social, but that is just masking their lack of ease, and in the long run they will appreciate the broader development which now they lack.

In a mixed programme, for the rather inexpert, here are dances which generally go well: Circassian Circle, Veleta, Barn Dance, St Bernard's Waltz, Dashing White Sergeant, Virginia Reel, Gay Gordons, Military Two Step.

And here is a good mixer. At any point in a dance in which couples are taking part make a sudden halt by stop-ping the music. Then let couples march round the room counter-clockwise, with girls on the inside, on the left arms of the boys. As they walk all begin to sing *Tipperary*. At the words 'Goodbye Piccadilly' partners shake hands. At 'Farewell Leicester Square' the girls continue their walk but the boys turn about and go round in a clockwise direction. At the end of the verse all halt: new couples say 'Hello' and shake hands – and the dance is taken up again.

POLISH YOUR DANCING

In any ordinary social dance with adults a knowledge of modern ballroom styles is essential. In a crowded winter club programme it is not easy to get proper tuition or practice, but during the slacker summer period there is often better opportunity. And, besides actual dances at the club, individual members usually find pleasant new occasions for dancing while they are on holiday. Here are guidance and practical hints for those who already have basic knowledge and would like to give more polish and style to their performance. It can form the basis for an 'advanced dance class'. Some members may be ambitious enough to work for a bronze medal, and the following instructions reach to that standard.

General Hints. One of the commonest faults is bending and swaying of the body, especially when making turns. Do not lean or bend or twist from the hips. Keep shoulders back and steady, and head upright. The man's right hand must not 'travel' – otherwise his partner gets no clear guidance from it; it should remain properly and comfortably placed so that, for instance, the slight pull on it necessary to turn a partner outward into a promenade position is immediately recognised. The right elbow should not be allowed to droop; if it is sufficiently high it gives the girl confidence and support.

Here is an absolutely basic rule for ballroom dancing – *every forward step must be made on the heel*. Look at your own waltz and quickstep with this in mind – does your heel first touch the floor when you step forward, or is it the ball of the foot or the flat sole? Correct footwork is the foundation of all good dancing, and you simply must know when to be on your heel and when to rise on to the ball of the foot. Related to the heel rule already given is another – *the heel of the foot from which a forward step is made must already be on the floor before the step is taken*. Remember also that the feet must not be turned outwards as in ordinary walking, but kept parallel with each other. Also, the feet must close together, really touching, whenever they are brought in at the conclusion of a step.

Make your backward steps deep; learners tend to step back – in a waltz for instance – just a few inches, instead of near a yard. Sideway steps should similarly be wide, the leg swinging outwards from the hip, like the leg of a pair of compasses opening swiftly. Your long back steps will always be taken on to the toes. And, at all other times, when you rise on to the toes, see that you really rise, though smoothly and evenly and not with a sudden jerk.

(In all the descriptions here given, the usual custom of referring only to the man's steps is followed – the girl's are usually the same but in reverse. General principles are the same for all dances).

The Waltz. Keep the body upright; step forward on the heel; make deep backward steps; make wide sideways steps; keep the right elbow up; hold the left arm comfortably extended, but do not force the girl's arms back.

See that you are backing against the Line of Dance at the halfway point of a Natural or a Reverse turn. (The

Line of Dance is the direction you are travelling along the side of a room. If you imagine it as a straight line on a clock-face from 6 o'clock to 12 o'clock, and you are facing towards 12 when you are travelling on the L-of-D, then you would be going backwards and facing 6 when 'backing the L-of-D').

In a Spin Turn be particularly careful not to lean forward, for this upsets the balance of your partner. Your heel, in the fifth step of this turn, should be between her feet, and you spin round on this heel, following it first with a side step, then with a back step and chassé.

Don't do a succession of simple Change Steps – forward; side; close, alternatively with right and left feet. This is dull and elementary. Learn, as quickly as possible, the Natural Turn, Reverse Turn, Spin Turn, Whisk, Hesitation, Back Outside Change, and introduce these.

In the Whisk, don't turn the body outward at the start. Begin it with a normal forward Left on heel and side Right, rising on to toes; then the Left foot is brought back behind the Right – still on the toes; Left heel sinks and the Right takes a forward step on its heel – followed by a quick-quick, Left-Right-Left sideways chassé, and finishing with a Right step forward *outside* the Right foot of the girl.

For the Back Outside Change – a useful and attractive movement – you begin with the first half of a Natural Turn, finishing backing the Line of Dance (facing 6 o'clock). Then Left back, heel going down; Right back, but with the body beginning to turn counter-clockwise; Left to the side, still on the toes (these three steps complete the figures 4, 5, 6 beats which are the second half of the Natural turn); Right forward, on heel.

The Hesitation is simple enough. In an ordinary Natural Turn the 4, 5, 6 beats of its second half are Left back, Right side, Left close. You will now be facing 'diagonal centre' (or 10.30 o'clock); and your weight will have gone on to the Left foot with the final step, so that the next – probably Change Step will begin with the Right. But in the Hesitation the Left foot closes to the Right in the 6th step, *but the weight is not put on to it*. Instead it pauses or hesitates alongside the Right and then pushes forward and so is able to start a Reverse Turn immediately, without the need for a Change Step to intervene – for the Reverse must begin with the Left foot.

The Quickstep. Keep the body upright; step well back; close the feet together; take good sideways steps on the chassés; never do a long series of Quarter Turns, or even Quarter Turns followed by Progressive Chassés. Just one or two are quite enough, and should immediately be followed by a Lockstep or a turn.

The basic Quickstep used to consist of just Quarter Turns (see *Rhythm Dancing* diagram, page 121). Nowadays the Progressive Chassé is always added, thus: Right forward (slow); Left side, close Right (quick quick); Left side (slow); Right back (slow); Left side, close Right (quick quick); Left side (slow); Right forward. The Quarter Turns are made between the forward and backward steps of the Right foot – for the forward you face diagonally to the wall (1.30 o'clock), for the backward you back diagonally to the centre (looking towards 4.30 o'clock).

See that you travel with wide steps on the Chassés.

In the Lockstep be sure that you are on your toes as the Left foot goes forward and the Right foot crosses behind it in its crisp quick-quick action. The Lockstep can be used frequently.

In the Spin Turn – just as in the Waltz – mind that you make the spin on your Right heel and keep shoulders steady and body upright.

The Natural Turn finishes with a 'Hesitation', in the manner of a Waltz Hesitation. It is performed as follows: *Step 1 – slow*. Right forward (facing 1.30 o'clock); *Step 2 and 3 – quick quick*. Left side, close Right (facing 6 o'clock, that is 'backing L-of-D'); *Step 4 – slow*. Left back, but you already begin to turn clockwise; *Step 5 – slow*. Step forward (facing 10.30 o'clock); *Step 6 – slow*. The Left foot, on the inside edge of its front part draws towards the Right. But the weight does not go on to it, and it does not even halt, but continues forward past the Right foot in a new slow step which thus forms Step 1 of the Reverse Turn which immediately follows.

Rhythm Dancing. This too-rarely studied style is becoming increasingly important because of more crowded dance floors and – so frequently – smaller floor spaces. As it is rarely possible to do a wide-ranging Foxtrot, and where you cannot even satisfactorily achieve a Waltz or Quickstep, Rhythm Dancing gives the answer. It is most simply understood as a slowed down Quickstep, and goes to the music of a Slow Foxtrot. The basic step is a simple combination of the Quarter Turn and the sideways Chassé – almost exactly as in the Quickstep, though now steps are very short and fairly slow.

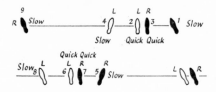

The diagram shows the man's steps. It will be seen that the dancer really travels along two parallel lines, making a *slow, quick-quick, slow* on each in turn. The parallel lines are no more than 18 inches apart. The Quarter (of a circle) Turn occurs between the forward step with the Right foot and the later backward step on to the rear parallel line, and the consequent slight turning of the body prevents the monotony of the otherwise continuous sideways travelling to the left. So, begin by turning the body slightly to the left and making a short step forward – arriving on the heel exactly as in ordinary walking – this is a *slow*. Follow by making a step of about 12 inches to the Left with the left foot and immediately closing the Right along to it – these are *quick-quick*. Continue with another step to the left with the Left foot – *slow*, and follow by turning slightly to the right and stepping back with the Right foot on to the second parallel line – this also is a *slow*, and begins an exact repetition of the sideways chassé steps as already described.

I   121

The important thing is to make all steps small. The Quarter Turns and Progressive Chassés, for example, should involve no steps longer than about 12 inches. But no more than two Quarter Turns should be done in quick succession – go straight into Conversation Piece, Back Corté, Pivot Turn, or Side Step.

In Conversation Piece you turn your partner into a promenade position and Left forward (slow); Right forward (slow); Left forward, Right close (quick quick). In Back Corté: Left back (slow); Right back (slow); Left back, Right foot merely drags an inch or two without stepping back (quick quick), giving the girl a chance to turn outwards in order to help the rhythm.

In the Natural Pivot Turn the Left foot makes only forward steps and you turn clockwise. In the Reverse Pivot Turn the Left foot still goes forward but you step backwards (instead of only sideways) on the Right and so turn counter-clockwise. In Side Step the Left steps to the side (slow), the Right foot closing to it with a swing but without touching the floor; the Right swings back into its original position and you step on to it (slow), this time the Left swings in towards it; the Left side, Right close (quick quick).

Remember not to stay long with each step but to move smoothly from one to another at frequent intervals.

Sequences. It is good to have some sort of instinctive programme or sequence of steps in any dance so that you get interesting variety, and adapt yourself readily to the shape of the room or the available space. So study your Waltz, Quickstep, Rhythm Dancing, from this angle and get used to a succession of steps – and the joining of them together – which seems to suit you.

With the Waltz you may do a couple of Change Steps (forward Right, side Left, Right close; Left forward, and so on) or better still go straight into a Natural Turn. Follow with Change Step and a Reverse Turn. After this you may put in a Whisk – and a Spin Turn. Remember that the Spin Turn, although it can be done along the side of a room, is especially useful at a corner, bringing you round into the new Line of Dance. Then, next time you begin a Natural Turn, you may conclude it as a Back Outside Change and follow with another Spin Turn. Next time, again, instead of the plain Natural Turn, finish with a Hesitation, and go right into a Reverse Turn. Use the Whisk freely.

With the Quickstep things happen so quickly that you will do best to concentrate for some time on a short sequence, perhaps of: two Quarter Turns and Progressive Chassés; Lockstep; Spin Turn; Quarter Turns again; Natural and Reverse Turns; Lockstep. Use the Lockstep frequently, it is particularly useful when you need to travel a little farther in order to get into a corner for a Spin Turn.

With Rhythm Dancing there is plenty of time to think, so that you can look well ahead and decide just what you are going to do next and how you will arrive into it – with forward or backward steps. You might begin with Quarter Turns and Progressive Chassés, and follow with – conversation Piece, Quarter Turns and Chassé; Reverse Pivot; Back Corté; Natural Pivot; Side Step. Remember not to stay long in any one step.

Finally, remember always to hold your partner firmly and lead her so that she knows what you intend to do and does not get confused.

JIVE SESSION

Few things nowadays will so surely pull a crowd of teen-agers into a club hall as a Jive Session, in which the newest teenage dance styles can be enjoyed. An event of this sort can be a most useful adjunct to a youth club, since it will almost certainly draw many outsiders who from this pre-liminary contact may advance still further by way of other club activities.

Many places, especially churches, have found it very rewarding to run such a Jive Session once a month, per-haps on a Saturday evening. It is not too difficult, in the sense that all that is needed is a good record player and a sufficient stock of reasonably up-to-date records – these can easily be borrowed from young enthusiasts. Refresh-ments are necessary too, but a club canteen committee or women helpers can easily cope – 'Hot dogs and Coffee' are ideal, though sandwiches serve well enough.

But perhaps the most vital requirement is an adequate supervision of the whole affair. Several adults, of strong personality and yet a sympathetic understanding must be available. One must be M.C. – though quite a young fellow or girl of the right type may suffice here; one or two others must be at the door, and generally responsible for good behaviour. It may be necessary to refuse admission to some young people; to enforce particular rules like 'No smoking in the hall'; to deal promptly and tactfully with outbreaks of indiscipline or misbehaviour. If such things are not firmly controlled the Jive Session may be wrecked. It is usually good to have some such rule as 'No re-admission after 9 o'clock'.

Don't be afraid of charging for admission. Young folk may even think the affair not worth attending unless you charge enough. But if the evening is well run, with almost nonstop liveliness, they will come and come again.

DANCE ELIMINATIONS

Coins. Give every girl a spring-type clothes peg. At the beginning of the dance her partner gives her some coin, which she clips to her dress. Then at each break in the music the M.C. calls out some coin – halfpenny, shilling, bun-penny, penny with a 1930 date, foreign coin, sixpence with a king's head – and the couples having those particular coins are out.

River Crossing. At one part of the room along the line of dance a strip, 'the river', perhaps two yards wide, is marked. When each couple reaches it the man must carry his partner across. When the music breaks off, any couple in midstream are eliminated. Several streams, of course, can be marked if there is likelihood that eliminations will not be frequent enough – or streams can be widened.

Balloon Grab. Balloons are scattered on the floor, and when the music stops each couple tries to grab one. Those who fail drop out. You must see that dancers always outnumber balloons – accidental bursts may help with this!

Pass the Book. One dancing couple carries a book. At any moment they may pass it to another pair – who must receive it without hesitation. Whoever holds the book when the music stops drops out. If there are more than twenty couples at the outset an additional book or two may be used. Any couple dropping a book must themselves pick it up.

Hats. Get some papier mâché hats. Use only one at the outset, putting it on the head of any boy as couples are dancing. The girl partner of the boy immediately takes off the hat and puts it on the head of some other boy – whose partner in turn similarly removes it and passes it to someone else. So the thing goes on, and when the music breaks off the couple with the hat are eliminated. Insist that partners stay together while getting rid of the hat; it is not permitted for a girl to leave her partner in order to put the hat on another boy.

As the thing warms up the leader may introduce two or three additional hats, which increases the excitement and eliminates the couples more rapidly. But when only about eight players remain it is best to return to just a single hat. When you are down to two couples stand these in the middle of the floor facing each other, and let the girls do the hat exchanging until the music break settles the winner.

Out by Numbers. When the music breaks the leader calls out a number (it must be an *even* number). The couples then rush to form rings containing exactly that number, and any who fail to get in drop out from the dance at the restart, when couples begin to go round afresh. It is well to tell how to get rings of a requisite number – let two couples join at the outset, letting in pair by pair until they have reached the number they want. When dancers are reduced to just four these two couples are the winners.

The leader needs to be careful of the numbers he calls, ensuring that some members are eliminated each time. Supposing there are forty taking part (twenty couples), this is how the calling might go: Six (four out, leaving thirty-six), Eight (four out, leaving thirty-two), Twelve (eight out, leaving twenty-four), Ten (four out, leaving twenty), Six (two out, leaving eighteen), Four (two out, leaving sixteen), Six (four out, leaving twelve), Eight (four out, leaving eight), Six (two out, leaving six), Four (two out, leaving four, the four Winners). To get a laugh, when music breaks and all wait for your number, call *Two*!

Seasonal Specials

Bonfire Night	New Year Party
Hallowe'en Party	Programme for Social
Christmas Party Games	

At particular seasons of the club year full and appropriate club programmes are needed if the celebrations are to give greatest enjoyment. This section deals with such occasions

BONFIRE NIGHT

Whatever the age of your members it is safe to assume that a lively celebration on November 5th will be enjoyed. So make detailed preparations in good time.

Get everyone collecting bonfire material, and ensure that it can be kept dry. Cardboard cartons can generally be obtained in quantities from tradespeople. Look around for chestnut trees, their brown leaves burn well, and folk who have them in their gardens are glad to be relieved of them since chestnut leaves are poisonous in compost heaps. Junk shops and secondhand dealers are often glad to be rid of old and broken furniture and bedding. Garages may hand over unwanted tyres. Builders and demolition people may offer you a pile of lumber.

Get a good site for your fire – safe, not too remote, but with the degree of privacy you want for such a special club occasion. How long beforehand you stack up your stuff must depend on so many local factors, but you want to be sure that it will blaze adequately at the appointed time.

Then fireworks. These need real supervision. Every club member might like to contribute some but they should not be let off indiscriminately, but be controlled entirely by one or two appointed folk. Here is general advice set out by the 'British Fireworks Manufacturers' Safety Association', under the heading *Enjoy your fireworks – safely*! You may like to put it up on the club notice-board in advance:

1. Read the instructions on each firework carefully and place in position as directed before lighting.
2. Light firework at arm's length, keep face well clear and don't lean over it.
3. Never put fireworks in pockets.
4. Keep fireworks in a covered box or container, take them out one at a time, and replace the lid before lighting.
5. Don't tamper with fireworks or try to make your own. This is silly, dangerous and illegal.
6. Never throw fireworks about.
7. Remember it is illegal for fireworks to be sold to children apparently under the age of thirteen or to let them off in the street.
8. Bonfires should be sited in open spaces. Never throw paraffin or petrol on to them and before leaving pour water on the embers.
9. Finally, a special word about pets. Keep them indoors and if of a nervous disposition, keep them away from the sight and sound of firework parties.

Plan supper too – roast potatoes, sausages, a hot drink? Whether you prepare these things on the spot, or at a convenient house, can be determined by your prior concern to get fullest enjoyment from the bonfire and the fireworks.

HALLOWE'EN PARTY

The ancient Hallowe'en, October 31st, is reputed to be a time when supernatural influences prevail; when ghosts and goblins walk abroad and witches wing through the night. So let your clubroom have the right atmosphere: dim red lights, skulls and bones, bats and black cats, fierce flashing eyes, orange and black decorations, candle holders made from carrots and potatoes. The traditional eatables are apples, nuts, doughnuts, and the drink should obviously be called Witches Brew. Spooky costumes can help the evening – sheets for ghosts, black rags for witches, horns and tails and masks for visitors from the dark regions.

If you like you can have appropriate invitation cards – there is plenty of scope for Hallowe'en imagination here. The cloakrooms may be labelled *Witches* and *Wizards*, perhaps with a box outside each, one marked 'Park broomsticks here' the other 'For fire and brimstone'. Nowadays younger club members often like to introduce 'gory hands', 'gang hide-outs', 'dead man gulch', and so on.

Here are other ideas: a Dress Parade, judged by witches; a Kitchen Band – various utensils serving as instruments; background music provided by 78 r.p.m. records played slowly; mock Fortune Telling. This latter is traditional for Hallowe'en as are, *Ducking for Apples* – apples floating in water which players try to take out with their teeth;

Mirror Gazing – a girl eating an apple while looking in a mirror was supposed to see her future boy-friend.

If premises and preparations allow there can be a *Terror Tour*, conducted by a Presiding Ghost – if he carries a feather duster he can give some uncanny shocks in the gloom by touching members of the party. The route may be equipped with the sort of things found in fun-fair tunnels – shrieks, whistles, groans, dangling strings and damp rags, luminous painted skeletons, crunchy sounds underfoot, dog whines.

Here are other suggestions:

Witches Broom Race – competitors astride sticks.

Goblin Choir – a singsong, squatting round a candle.

Ghost Story – a similar dim circle, with someone telling a well-prepared tale.

Black Cat Game – can be played by teams or individuals. A definition is given, and the word beginning with *cat* has to be guessed. For instance: It throws stones (catapult), It crawls on leaves (caterpillar), It sings or screeches (catgut), It gets you in the nose (catarrh), It dangles on a tree (catkin), It's a slogan (catchword), It's a disease (catalepsy), It's a burying place (catacomb).

Hallowe'en Horrors – all sit in a Witches Circle, in the dark. The Chief Witch tells how at last Hallowe'en a Club member died of fright, and proceeds to pass round relics, which go from hand to hand in the dark. 'Here,' she mumbles, 'are his poor dear eyes' and hands on two large grapes or jelly cubes; 'His poor dear heart' (lump of cooked liver); 'Tongue' (sliver of meat); 'Hands' (rubber gloves filled with wet sand); 'Lungs' (damp sponge); 'Teeth' (odd ones from a butcher); 'Stomach' (semi-inflated balloon); 'All the brain he had' (bit of tangled cord).

Ghost Parade – this should be taken in Conga fashion, but in partial gloom. The leader calls at intervals: 'On heels; on toes; feet turned in', and so on.

CHRISTMAS PARTY GAMES

New Year Auguries. Put three firm-standing cups or mugs on a table at one end of the room. Each should be half-filled: one with water, one with milk, one with vinegar. Players, one at a time, are blindfolded; make their way up to the table; find and dip a finger in one mug; suck their finger. According to which mug each person finds will be his or her augury for the coming year. Water – denotes no particular change; milk – likely to become engaged or married; vinegar – likely to become engaged or married and to find the course of true love far from smooth.

To ensure that a blindfolded person does not know beforehand where to find a particular liquid the mugs can be re-arranged as he approaches, by the leader. The leader should, of course, have made a preliminary announcement about the auguries, and invited only unmarried folk to take part.

Jimbo. A pencil and paper are provided for each person – ordinary quarto typing pages will serve. Each paper is divided into sixteen 'squares' by three upright and three transverse lines. Each person, preferably seated at a table, writes the Christian name of some person present in each square – if possible a different name in each. The square into which a name goes is entirely optional, no-one should copy his neighbour. The leader meanwhile will have written perhaps twenty-four names, assuming so many are present, each on a separate small slip of paper or card. When all are ready he sits at the front; shakes the slips in a box, and draws them out haphazardly one at a time, calling out each name in turn. As a name is called each player who has it on his own paper puts a small piece of macaroni on that square (a packet of macaroni is a convenient means of supplying each player with sixteen 'marking pieces'). As soon as any player has filled in four squares in a straight line – vertically, horizontally or diagonally – he calls out 'Jimbo'. A point is scored to him or he may be given a chocolate or trifling prize. Then all papers are cleared; the leader shakes up his box of name slips, and begins to call out a new round.

Partners. Players are divided into couples, and each boy is instructed to talk to his partner for two minutes. At the end of this time the girls go out of the room – or better still sit in a cluster behind the boys' backs, so that they cannot be seen. Then each boy in turn is asked a series of questions, to discover how observant he was of his partner. For instance: What was her name? The colour of her dress? Of her eyes? How was her hair done? Did she have a wrist-watch? A necklace? Make-up?

It Was You Said That. Players sit in a ring. A volunteer goes outside. Then each in the ring whispers something about him to his, or her, right-hand neighbour. It might be: 'He has such lovely eyes', 'His mother has to drag him from bed each morning', 'He's terribly clever'. Then-everyone moves to different seats so that the person outside cannot know who was on anyone's right.

He is recalled and goes to any person, asking, 'What did you hear about me?' The person tells him, and the boy then goes to any other in the ring and demands: 'Did you say that about me?' The one might reply: 'No, but I heard that you put your hair in curlers every Friday.' The boy goes to some other – continuing similarly until he chances on the right person – with whom he then changes places. This new person goes out of the room; new whispers are exchanged; everyone changes seats – and the game proceeds as before.

Celebrity Interviews. Number all those taking part, then explain that even numbers are Celebrities and odd numbers are Reporters. If the numbers have been written on slips of paper and mixed before handing out, so much the better. The Reporters must then find their quarries and begin. Each Celebrity must be interviewed by the person whose number is one lower – Number 3 interviews Number 4, and so on. The Reporters, with pencils and papers, have to secure answers to six questions. **1.** What is your name? **2.** If you could change it what would you prefer? **3.** Describe your ideal girl (or boy). **4.** What change would you most like to see in this town, or city? **5.** What do you do with all your money? **6.** What do you think of the present company?

Two or three clear-voiced Sub-Editors should have been chosen who will now read out the Interviews, and the leader or Chief Editor decides on the best, and awards a prize – for the couple.

Quickwits. Try these on the party:

I walked the length of the street and counted forty houses on my left hand; then I turned round and came back and counted forty houses on my right. How many houses did I count? (forty – I was counting the same ones coming back).

Punctuate: It was not and I said but or. (It was not 'and' I said, but 'or'.)

How many camels were there in the line when: Two camels were in front of a camel; two were behind a camel, and one was in the middle. (Three.)

What would be your relationship to your brother-in-law's wife's grandmother's husband? (You would be his grandson.)

At Barney Steeple I passed three people. They were neither men, women, nor children. What were they? (A man, a woman, a child.)

What word signifying a household material beginning with p is pronounced differently when it belongs to a north European country? (Polish, polish.)

Suppose you are a taxi driver. A passenger jumps in with a suitcase and asks to be driven to the railway. On the way, there is a hold-up. The passenger jumps out and runs for the train, just catching it – but he has left his case in the taxi. The taxi driver doesn't know what train he has taken; the passenger doesn't know the taximan. What was the driver's name? (Your name – we began 'Suppose *you* were . . .).

Wanted. Split your players into four teams – by birthdays in each quarter of the year is an easy method, slight adjustments will equalise numbers. Put the teams in different corners of the room, each with a leader. A Scorer sits at a table in the middle of the room, with pencil and paper, and a list of things he is going to call out one at a time.

He calls: 'A comb' – and the first leader who produces one from his team and dashes with it to the centre table scores a point. When the leaders are back to their places a new thing is called from the Scorer's list – and so the game goes on.

Here are suggestions for the list: Necklace, Postage Stamp, Threepenny piece, Lady's left shoe, Wooden door key, Beads, Sixpence and a Shilling. Man's sock, Necktie wrapped in a handkerchief, Lapel Badge, Ear-rings, Man's shoelace, Compact. There is no need to explain that, for instance, 'shoelace' need not be taken out of a shoe before the leader brings it to the table!

Famous Persons and Things. Each person has pencil and paper. Around the room, prominently displayed you will have placed twenty objects, each clearly numbered. Players are allowed about ten minutes to go round and guess at the famous people who are suggested by the various objects. Here is a possible list: **1.** Slipper (Cinderella); **2.** Firework (Guy Fawkes); **3.** Lamp (Florence Nightingale); **4.** Small hatchet (George Washington); **5.** Kite and 'thunderstorm' written on paper (Benjamin Franklin); **6.** Spider's web (Robert Bruce); **7.** Tub (Diogenes); **8.** Apple (Eve, Newton or William Tell); **9.** Fiddle (Nero); **10.** Silver cup (Benjamin); **11.** Postage stamp

THE YOUTH CLUB IDEAS BOOK

(Rowland Hill); **12.** Burned cake (King Alfred); **13.** Plum (Jack Horner); **14.** Cigar (Winston Churchill); **15.** Telescope and Eye shade (Nelson); **16.** Umbrella (Neville Chamberlain); **17.** Picture or drawing of long hair (Samson or Absalom); **18.** Cup labelled 'hemlock' (Socrates); **19.** Photograph or picture of a dove (Noah or Picasso); **20.** Globe or picture of world labelled 'round in 80' (Jules Verne).

Tongue Teasers. Prize-giving with Vice-Presidents present; I oil all the oil holes; It's a tricky sticky wicket; Some summers Sam simmered; Sally slipped on slippery slippers; Which witch whistled; A white-washed wristwatch.

Fetch the Alphabet. The Scorer sits at one end of the room while all the players are divided into two teams sitting on opposite sides. If four teams, let them sit in the corners of the room, with the Scorer at the centre. Each team has a leader, and only he or she must approach the table. The aim of each team is to send to the table, one thing at a time only, something beginning with each letter of the alphabet as it is called by the Scorer. The Scorer has the letters of the alphabet written in two or four vertical columns on his paper. He awards scores as the objects are brought in by putting against the appropriate column, 2 or 1 – which is the score earned by the first two leaders to reach him. The letters, of course, will not be called in proper alphabetic order – or teams will be looking ahead all the time and preparing. It is much more satisfactory if players are not allowed to go out of the room in order to fetch things. The Scorer should cross off the letters in his list as they are used up. He should frequently announce scores, so as to keep rivalry keen.

World Citizens. Allow everyone five minutes in which to write down as many States of the United Nations as they can, and give a small prize to the one with the longest list – there are well over one hundred.

Musical Snatch. Before starting you will have placed round the room, or even outside, various small portable objects – shoe, book, hat, brush, bucket, broom, and so on. Players may stroll round and see them.

Then music begins, and all taking part walk round in couples with linked arms, or dance. When the music breaks off the leader calls out for any one object, and the first couple to snatch it scores a point. The leader retains the object, and the music restarts. When all the things have been snatched that couple have won who have snatched most objects.

NEW YEAR PARTY

Your club is pretty sure to have something of the sort, so here are varied items and ideas which you may work in to give really distinctive character to the party. If you are a church club you may meet on New Year's Eve, and carry over with a brief 'Watchnight Service' into the new year.

New Year Comes in. Three ancient customs can bring memorable novelty to the early part of the new year:

One. Open the back door, to let the Old Year out – all of you can crowd to see it go! Open the front door to let the New Year in.

Two. Ensure that 'a dark man' is the first to cross your threshold in the New Year – you can choose a suitable person and arrange for him to be at the front door at the right moment. When he enters he should be carrying the three traditional gifts: a piece of coal, to ensure the house has comfort; bread, to ensure food; a Bible, to bring a blessing.

Three. Drink a Wassail Cup. To make it mix 1 pint orange juice, ½ pint grapefruit juice, 1 oz. sugar, 2 tablespoons lemon juice. As you toast the New Year let all say 'Wass hael' which is old Saxon for 'To your health'. You might sing 'Here we come a-wassailling'.

Calendar. This is a sort of team game, for multiples of twelve, so at least twenty-four must take part. Prepare two, or more, sets of twelve paper slips or cards, writing the name of a month of the year on each. Shuffle them all, and without any explanation distribute them at random among the people in the room – those who do not get slips cannot, of course, take part. Then announce that the winning group will be the twelve who first form themselves into a straight line along one of the walls, with their name-slips held in front of them and all their months in correct order.

January Happenings. Ask for volunteer groups of four or five who will compete in dramatising various events which happened in January. Here are some such happenings: Cromwell dissolved Parliament, 1655; London docks opened, 1805; Joan of Arc born 1412; James Watt born 1736; Robert Burns, 1759; Mozart, 1756; Whitehall ceremony commemorating execution of Charles I; Don Quixote published 1605; Thames frozen over 1855; Edward VII crowned 1901; Queen Victoria died 1901; Warsaw entered by Russians 1945.

One way of dealing with this is to announce a subject and let each team in turn dramatise or mime it. Another method – give each team a list and let them decide which thing they will act out, if they mention no names the audience can guess what it is.

Monthly Talky. Have three piles of paper slips. In the first pile each slip bears the name of a boy who is present; the second pile has the girls' names; the third pile consists of the months of the year. Draw at random one paper from each, then announce, for example: '*John Smith* will talk with *Mary Brown* on a *June* topic.' All the couples immediately get together, conversing for two minutes on any topics suggested by the name of the month allotted to them. You can make fresh draws as often as you like – and it is rather fun, at the end, to have people tell what subjects they linked with their months.

New Year Resolves. Squat in a ring, around a red candle burning safely in a large dish or pan. Let each think of some personal fault which he would like to be rid of in the New Year; then write it on a slip of paper and burn it at the candle. Next let each write some worthwhile resolve he would like to keep from the beginning of this New Year. To signify the resolve he will light a small white candle – part of a ring around the red one. He will then hand his slip, sealed in an envelope, with his name outside, to the club leader – who will retain it, and hand it back on some occasion in the future, perhaps on the first day of the next month, to check whether the resolve has been kept.

PROGRAMME FOR SOCIAL

Round about April it is pretty sure that members will appreciate another social before the light nights come. Plan it to have a good mixture of dances and a sprinkling of games, so that there is something for every taste. Encourage everybody to have a go at every item – nothing kills social atmosphere more than refusal by various sections to participate in anything but their particular favourite forms of amusement.

For dances – The newest styles of course, perhaps with eliminations. Then familiar things like Veleta, Gay Gordons, St Bernard's Waltz, Barn Dance – and maybe Square Tango, Madison, Quickstep, Cha-cha.

And games – here are a few suggestions:

Time Test. All sit in a ring. Announce that girls must stand up when they judge one minute to have passed, and boys when two minutes have passed. Give them the 'from now' word and keep your eye on your watch (it is assumed that no wall clock is visible). Say nothing until all the girls are standing, but note which one was nearest to the sixty seconds. Do the same for the boys. At the end tell who were the winners.

Musical Numbers. Let all march or dance round. When the music stops call out a number – and players must form into groups of that number. Those who fail drop out.

Dumb Crambo. An ancient game, but good. Two teams.

One goes out, and the *in* settles on some simple word which has to be guessed – it might be 'rain'. The others come in and are told the word rhymes with 'strain'. Then they go in a huddle and return to mime what they hope the word may be – perhaps 'crane'. Learning they are wrong they try again – perhaps miming 'pain', again unsuccessfully. So it goes on until they get 'rain', or give up – and teams change over. Here are useful words: dine, fine, pine, sign, line; fare, wear, rare, chair, pair; boat, coat, float, dote, wrote; speed, steed, feed, greed, weed; rest, guessed, test, nest, pest.

Queues. Have six trade words, on the walls, at intervals, each representing a different shop: Baker, Grocer, Chemist, Butcher, Stationer, Hardware. Let players stroll round to music. When this stops call out something which has to be bought – it might be 'Rice'. All dash to the appropriate 'shop', and queue in pairs. The last pair, or two couples, are 'out' and the game restarts. So, eventually, only the winners are left. Get your list of 'purchases' well mixed. It might run: Chopper, liver, envelopes, buns, cough mixture, sausage roll, toothpaste, cup and saucer, ballpoint pen.

Continuing Interests

Samaritan Squad	Debating
Service and Work Camps	A Poetry Group
Friendliness Adventure	Ballet
Helping the Deaf and	Photographer at Large
Dumb	Sketching
Red Cross Kits	Climbing Do's and Dont's
Help! Help!	Speleology, or Cave
Why not Gardening	Exploration
Camping	Adventure Planning
Voice Production	Jumping
Speaking in Public	Canoeing
Taking Church Services	Cross-country Running

Most of the ideas in the early part of this book have to do with single occasions and single programmes. In this section longer term projects are dealt with – interests and activities which, when once started, can provide continuing effort and planning, with real achievement as a result.

SAMARITAN SQUAD

A winter blizzard and freeze-up can bring a multitude of problems for which many people are completely unprepared. Some suffer extreme hardship and even danger, and help when it is given is often improvised and tardy.

Would it be possible for your club to organize itself so that in special circumstances of need your members could promptly put into action plans already worked out for just such an emergency? The Police, the Fire Service, the Red Cross, Civil Defence, Mountain Rescue teams, all know exactly what to do when a crisis arises in which they can play a part.

Old people living alone perhaps suffer most distress. Their paths need to be cleared; frozen pipes perhaps thawed, or plumbers fetched; fuel brought into the house; essential shopping done. Many homes have no menfolk, and heavy work like snow shovelling needs to be done there. Doctors and nurses often have to make hazardous journeys alone, and maybe dig themselves out of drifts unhelped – a couple of sturdy teenagers with a spade and some old sacks, and power to push, could be gratefully carried on such wintry occasions. So envisage all such possibilities, maybe splitting your town or area into sections with a 'Samaritan Squad' responsible for each. List down the people most likely to need help, and the sort of help likely to be required, then determine in advance just what equipment and plans you will need to get into action without delay.

Snow is not the only hazard – floods, gales, breakdown of water or gas or electricity supplies, even protracted drought, may give rise to emergency situations. Consider all such things in relation to the needs of those least able to help themselves. In country districts farmers often have special problems of their own, like those of rush harvesting – there may be opportunity here for your club.

In one or two parts of England the early Christian

symbol of the fish is being brought back with a new significance. Your club may like to adapt this. Supposing, for instance you supply the co-operating old people and invalids of your district each with a card on which is drawn the fish symbol, with the understanding that whenever help of any sort is required the card shall be displayed in the window. Your 'Samaritans' can then make a rule of passing every day along their particular 'beats', looking out for the cards. When one is seen a call at the house is immediately made.

A single week's investigation of 'Samaritan jobs' within easy reach of a home counties youth club revealed the following: **1.** Grass patch in front of house, which crippled owner could not keep trimmed; **2.** Decrepit invalid chair which needed cleaning, oiling, overhauling; **3.** Lonely old lady unable to do anything about her garden fence which was broken; **4.** Man with injured back unable temporarily to dig his allotment; **5.** Boy in hospital without relatives who could visit him; **6.** Person going blind who had trouble with shopping; **7.** Polio sufferer who could only get to church if someone wheeled her; **8.** Family going on holiday worried about care of pets they had to leave behind; **9.** Invalid, seemingly forgotten by all, and desperately longing for visitors.

The teenagers of that particular club were able to give help in every case. Might it not be a good idea for your own members to make an investigation in their own locality, and to plan action. In the early days, especially look out for jobs – like mending a fence – which can be completed at one go, and so do not loom as a continuing and possibly burdensome obligation on an individual.

SERVICE AND WORK CAMPS

Here is a sphere in which opportunities grow year by year and which calls out all the adventurous best which is in young people – altruism, physical effort, imaginative construction, religious concern. Teenagers wanting a holiday with a difference can certainly find opportunities here.

Broadly speaking, camps or working parties of this sort are formed to do specific jobs. For the service the members give they have free keep, and sometimes even a little pocket money. The work they undertake may be afforestation; fruit harvesting; helping refugees; renovating old or constructing new buildings – like churches, hostels, club centres; nature conservation; removing eyesores. Such tasks may be done either in Britain or abroad. Often they are undertaken by groups of mixed nationalities, with members giving what time they can, from as little as a single weekend to as much as a whole summer vacation.

Opportunities and requirements are, by the nature of things, always changing, and an interested club should ask for advice and information at the time required from their local Education Authority, Youth Organisation Headquarters, Church Youth Department.

Here may be a way of solving holiday problems for some of your members.

Voluntary Service Overseas. The V.S.O. organization offers much more ambitious scope. It provides opportunities for young people – though they be without technical or professional qualifications – to give free work for one year in some undeveloped country. It is a wonderful way of 'youth speaking to youth' in the building up of a happier world family.

FRIENDLINESS ADVENTURE

You can call it *'Frenvens'* if you like. The idea is that small groups of your club members equip themselves so that they can visit lonely old people and give them a pleasant hour or two. Three is an ideal group for the purpose, and they, together with the other groups, should do some careful preparation. During this period of 'training' enquiries should be made by club leader, or through Church or other channels, to discover the people who would be likely to welcome them in their homes.

For instance there may be a bed-ridden old lady who would be delighted to receive a visit from three bright teenage girls. They might bring her flowers, and arrange them under her direction; they might do a little ironing for her. And they could certainly make her a cup of tea, and have one themselves – maybe with cakes they have made and brought along. Could they also comb the cat or clean the birdcage? A little general cleaning and dusting might also be appreciated – especially if they carefully polished one or two prominent photographs and asked all about them.

Or it might be an old man, largely house-bound, glad to welcome all-too-rare visitors, in the forms of three friendly club boys. Knowing something about him beforehand they might might have decided that what he would most like to know would be how the local football team played last Saturday. But other things could come in: maybe windows cleaned, shoes polished, mats shaken. The boys, also, might have fun and give pleasure by preparing a 'club supper', with warm drink, hot dogs, or anything else they could have brought along with them. They would certainly want him to tell them how he used to spend his spare time when he was their age.

There are so many ways in which a *Frenvens* group could enliven their visit. First of all, of course, they must be prepared to be good listeners, for old people love to reminisce and to have someone to hear them appreciatively. But the teenagers can, besides, take things along with them – other than items for supper. A club scrapbook can be interesting. So can tape recordings of club features, of church services, of greetings and messages spoken especially for the occasion by friends or acquaintances who are themselves unable to visit the old person. Playing a few records may be a good idea – though the record-player may have to be taken.

Old folk may like the chance to play a game – dominoes, draughts, cards, chess, even ludo or snakes-and-ladders. If your club folk do 'hand jiving', marking out dance rhythm with movements of arms, fingers, palms, fists, then this sitting-still dance can be introduced to an old person, for it really can be fun as well as being a novel and healthful exercise. There are, additionally, heaps of sitting-still party games.

Perhaps a little hymn-singing might go well, and it may be necessary to take hymnbooks. Then, almost certainly a prayer would be appreciated at the close of it. It may be possible to introduce a version of a colourful club epilogue or orison, maybe with a lighted candle or picture and a reciting of the 23rd Psalm. But don't tire the old people.

The measure of enjoyment must be what they like, and not necessarily what the teenagers themselves would like to do.

Be sure to have frequent consultations between your *Frenvens* group, so that experiences can be pooled and techniques developed. Tackled sincerely and humbly hardly anything your young folk can undertake will be more rewarding than these ventures into friendliness.

HELPING THE DEAF AND DUMB

Deaf and dumb people are not so conspicuous and recognisable as are blind folk, and so often suffer from lack of understanding and sympathy in their dreadful handicap. For instance, few realise how difficult it is for the deaf and dumb boy and girl to gain education – even when adult he or she may never have progressed beyond the attainments of a normal youngster of eight or nine. If, in your district, it is possible to make contact with deaf and dumb organizations or individuals – perhaps through information supplied at your local government offices, then club members may devise ways of giving friendship and service. Learning sign language, for instance, in order to converse with handicapped people might be one way – it will not be easy, and might take a couple of hours a week for a year, but it could be so rewarding. Teaching chess to an elderly deaf man could be less arduous but very worthwhile. Other practical ways of serving the deaf and dumb might well show up from your genuinely concerned enquiries.

RED CROSS KITS

When, anywhere in the world, there is a sudden great disaster, such as an earthquake, flood, or hurricane, it is almost taken for granted that Red Cross aid will quickly be available. What is less widely known is that groups of young people can be of very practical help in ensuring that supplies are ready when they are needed. Suppose, for instance, that hundreds of children on some Pacific island lose homes and all they possess through some terrible tidal wave. The Red Cross will have 'relief kits' available, each kit consisting of a bag ready packed with the essential things those children need. The kits cannot well be prepared when disaster has come, they must be in readiness for immediate distribution. Why should not your club help prepare such kits?

It is important that the following list of contents should be strictly adhered to: 1 cake of soap in plastic box, 1 toothbrush in a plastic tube holder, 1 wash flannel, 1 comb (these first four in a plastic bag), 1 unbreakable polythene mug, 1 plastic spoon, 2 men's size handkerchiefs, hair ribbon, rustless safety-pins, small ball of string, 1 sharpened pencil, 1 notebook (without metal spiral binding), 1 unbreakable all-plastic toy, 1 face towel, 1 ball.

The contents of each kit, which should be new or in first-class condition, should be packed in the authorised calico draw-string bag. The Red Cross emblem should be sewn on the centre of the bag.

But, make inquiries from your local Red Cross.

HELP! HELP!

General Hints. Every young person should have some training in First Aid and so on. Such training can best be covered in one or more Courses. The Club Committee should carefully consider the matter, with particular relation to local circumstances and the sort of specialist people who may be prepared to help – Doctor; Police; Nurse; member of St John's or Red Cross; Fire Service official; A.A. or R.A.C. representative; Coastguard, Lifeboatman.

Here are various aspects of the broad subject: *Accidents on the Road* – How to deal with bleeding, and with fractures; what to do about other traffic when the road is obstructed by damaged vehicle or injured people. *Accidents at Home* – What to do for cuts, burns, scalds, electric shocks. *Fire* – How to act when a chimney is on fire; when a person's clothes are ablaze; when an overturned lamp, sparks from a grate, or something similar, has started flames in a room. *Nursing* – Looking after invalids; making beds; preparing diets; taking temperatures; general nursing. *Accidents in the Water* – Methods of dealing with boating accidents, bathing emergencies, mishaps on the ice; artificial respiration. *General* – Ways of getting medical or other help in quickest possible time; carrying the injured; improvising stretchers, splints and suchlike; preparation and storing of first-aid equipment.

First-Aid. Though this is as useful as anything which can be taught in a club it should not therefore be assumed that it will be the most popular. A great deal will depend on the personality of the instructor and the amount of interest and enthusiasm he, or she, manages to infuse into the subject.

The best plan is to arrange a short course of perhaps six lessons. They can be taken by a qualified club leader, or by some doctor, nurse, or other competent volunteer. The instructor will naturally arrange and conduct the classes in the manner which best suits his experience.

Preliminary interest of the club may be roused by installing a first-aid box on the premises. This should contain at least – lint, for dressing wounds; cotton wool, for pads on dressings; 1-inch roller bandages, for fingers; 2½-inch bandages for head or limbs; 3-inch bandages for limbs or body; triangular bandages for arm-slings; small safety pins; scissors; smelling salts; sal volatile; iodine or other antiseptic.

The 'public installation' of this box should prompt many members to join the first-aid class, especially if you further emphasise the importance of exact knowledge by putting up by the box a list of 'Emergency Addresses' – Nearest doctors, hospital, chemist, ambulance station, police station, fire alarm.

The lectures themselves – which should be plentifully illustrated by chart, blackboard, and 'exhibits' – should always include practical work like bandaging, stretcher training, resuscitation methods. Knowledge of anatomy is useful and interesting, but it is not the essential knowledge needed in first-aid. Similarly, sick-nursing, which should not be thought the sphere of girls alone, should not be intruded during a first-aid course, but treated as a separate activity which can usefully follow the first course.

Members must from the outset be given a sense of the urgency and importance of the knowledge they are acquiring, and of the fundamentals – in accident or emergency bleeding must be stopped; the patient must not be made worse by improper position, movement, or treatment; a written message should be sent to a doctor if possible; the patient should be treated kindly and gently.

In planning your first-aid bear in mind local conditions,

and give at an early stage the special knowledge most likely to be of use in your district. Drowning accidents may be prevalent, or road mishaps, or sprains and hiking blisters, or sunstroke. The first-aid student values his knowledge vastly more when once there has been a genuine opportunity to make use of it.

WHY NOT GARDENING

Gardening is not a common club activity, but it can be a source of revenue, and interest, and education too, providing a few of your club members can be made keen enough. A piece of allotment may not seem very romantic, but it gains a great deal when it belongs to the club and your members themselves decide just what to do with it. Better still is a piece of ground round the club's premises, or an enclosed garden where fruit-trees and flowers, and even ornamental trees and a lawn can be cultivated. Many householders, unable to cope, would gladly hand over an untended garden to be developed by young people.

The essential thing in order that gardening shall be a successful activity, is that your members shall have a keen interest in the results of their labour – they must be able to play on the lawn; eat the fruit at winter banquets; make the jam for use in the canteen; sell the vegetables for a specific club fund. Or, alternatively, there can be a community service motive – achieving a regular income for a particular charity; supplying the owner, or a group of old or needy people, with garden produce; stimulating interest – and winning prizes – in local flower-shows; maintaining a garden which can be a showplace and model in the locality.

In order that gardening can be a shared and regular activity it is necessary to have a clear time-table of work throughout the year. Here is a brief summary of what needs to be done month by month:

January – Clearing up month. Get accumulated rubbish ready for burning. Digging empty ground, forking over flower-beds. Possible planting of early potatoes, peas, broad beans; *February* – Press bulbs into ground if frost causes them to rise. If weather is right sow hardy annuals. This is the month for plenty of digging, and for sowing the chief vegetables; *March* – A busy month – preparing ground for flowers; manuring. Sowing onions, cabbages, peas. Planting more potatoes, broad beans, parsley, radishes, lettuce; *April* – The time for outdoor flower sowing; lupins, sweet peas, marigolds, nasturtiums, sunflowers. Rhubarb can be put in; marrow seeds under glass; green crops and other vegetables can still be planted; *May* – Flowers should be bedded out, and bulbs which are finished should be lifted out and stored for next autumn. French beans can be sown, and runner beans; *June* – This is the month when flowers are 'on show'. Among the vegetables, potatoes should be earthed up; celery can be planted, and more French beans; *July* – The flowers will need trimming and tidying, and many staking for support. Rake and clean beds. Overhaul pea and runner bean sticks. Earth up and tidy other vegetables; *August* – Perennial flowers may be divided at the roots for propagation. Keep weeds down. Roses can be budded; chrysanthemums manured and cleared of insects. Sowings of cabbages for next spring's planting out may be made; *September* – Water dahlias and thin out foliage. Clean up flower-beds. Thin out turnips, and dig such potatoes, early carrots, onions, as are ready. Keep the hoe busy to check weeds; *October* – This is the best transplanting month. Seedlings of spring-blooming flowers may be planted out. Deep dig or trench empty vegetable ground in readiness for next year. Earth up celery. Plant out winter cabbages; *November* – Move rose-trees if necessary and do other planting of trees. All heavy digging should be done before frost sets in, and whole garden generally tidied. Look over green crops and remove vermin; *December* – Manure can be forked in and general cleaning up completed, with any digging not yet done. Protection against frost may be necessary with some plants.

CAMPING

General Hints. Many leaders like to take their young people camping, and unless they have had previous experience tend to be a little anxious about permits and insurances. Let it be said at once that the really essential requirement for any such camping is a competent leader.

First, *permits*. If you have a Scout troop, or something similar, permission will certainly have to be obtained from the officers of your local association. They will need to know a great deal about the personnel and general arrangements. If regulations of this sort do not apply to you, two other basic permissions probably do – the consent of the owner of the land on which you propose to camp, and the knowledge and full agreement of all the parents concerned with your party.

Second, *insurance*. It is always advisable to have insurance cover for groups of your people. Probably your club, church, Sunday school, already has adequate cover. So find out if your weekend camp is properly safeguarded. Check also, if you use a lorry for transport, that the owner's insurance policy and licence entitle him to carry both equipment and passengers.

The real safeguard, of course, is the leader himself and his knowledge or experience of camping, with its necessity for clear rules and discipline if the camp is to yield all the fun and benefits that it should.

What to Carry to Camp. Whatever sort of camping your members may be proposing it is helpful to provide them with a list of things they are likely to need. Here is an example of what a boy with a rucksack might pack: tent, sleeping bag, ground sheet, pyjamas, shirt, socks, shorts, sweater, handkerchiefs, plimsols and spare laces, needles and so on, waterproof, towel, swimming trunks, toilet requisites, matches, two plates, mug, knife and fork with dessert spoon, tea-towel, first-aid pack, diary, with compass and map. In packing a rucksack remember to get the soft things against your back, with plates and cups and hard things on the outer side. Have the waterproof readily available; a tent is better placed on top of a rucksack than beneath it. Total weight, of course, must be determined by age and size of boy or girl – don't overstrain. In judging the efficiency and adequacy of kit, see that nothing inessential is carried, but that there shall be all that is needed for sleeping out, for eating and cooking, for toilet, and changes of clothes.

Moving Camp. A settled camp for a whole club is one thing; a camping trek or holiday for just two or three is quite another. In the one you stay put; the total equipment is transported merely at the beginning and end, and in between all take their turns at the various chores. In the other sort of camping, you move on day by day – walking, cycling, canoeing, punting, and make camp all over again each night.

To be mobile, choice of clothing, and the weights of everything, are extremely important. Especially get the right footwear for the job, and a really good sleeping bag – if you don't sleep well and snugly there won't be much fun!

Start early each day, and arrive at the new site in the afternoon. Pitch your tent with an eye to shelter, water supply, morning sunshine, and sanitary convenience. You may have covered the route beforehand, and planned stops; if not, allow time for this. Don't reckon on tramping more than ten miles a day, with a normal load – something less than thirty pounds on your back. A cyclist might do forty miles each day, without undue speed or strain. Boating is more difficult to forecast, for winds, currents, shallows, locks, may all bring complications.

Old hands learn knacks which make easier meals – saving time, making best use of heat, reducing necessary utensils. At breakfast, for instance you can heat your tea water then make porridge and keep it warm over the hot water while you fry your sausages. Then finish off the porridge, and as you eat it bring the tea dixie to the boil – a plate over the sausages will have kept in their heat.

VOICE PRODUCTION

Public speaking contests, debates, drama, quizzes, are

prominent in club programmes – and all of them demand clear and effective speaking. Yet few club members get any advice on how to make their voice audible and interesting, beyond just 'Speak up!' and 'Don't mumble'. Things are slightly better when young speakers are told: 'Talk to the back row of your audience', 'Separate your words', 'Speak more slowly', 'Get final consonants firm and clear', 'Don't begin every sentence at the same pitch', 'Vary the melody pattern of sentences'.

But even that advice does not really get you very far, for it has nothing in it about voice production which is the major, fundamental problem. So, if a few of your club members are likely to be interested, let them do some real systematic study in this matter. Here are a few practical tips on what they can do:

Good breathing is essential. Practise filling the lungs from the bottom upwards by consciously depressing the diaphragm. Relaxation of the whole body is similarly important for easy speaking; though there is one exception worth remembering – the forceful beginning of a sentence is helped if at the moment of utterance the abdominal muscles are pulled in.

Two points are of outstanding general importance: *One*, the lips should be flexible and much used; *Two*, the lower *jaw*, and the tongue inside it, should have much practice in dropping deeply, so that the mouth opens downwards instead of sideways.

The doctor orders: 'Say *ah*' so that the mouth opens deeply with tongue flattened down and so that he can see clearly into the throat. That *ah* sound is invaluable for the speaker. If you follow it with an *oo* sound, in front of a mirror, you can ensure that the lips push forward, the top one curling up, so that they are almost square. A combination of this *ah – oo* gives the correct *ou* sound (compare 'how now brown cow' said in this way, and followed by the faulty alternative sideways spreading of the mouth with no dropping of the jaw).

Do much practice for particular sounds, pushing voice and lips forward. Here is an *ah* exercise: 'I will take heart, and make a start.' for *oo*: 'Bloomsburying, Bloomsburying, who will go a-Bloomsburying.' For *ou*: 'Down they went without a sound.'

It is good to find your own exercises from familiar prose or poetry and strongly emphasise the *ah*, *oo* and *ou* sounds exaggerating and lengthening them as much as you please. Speaking in front of a mirror is particularly useful for you can then ensure that the lips come forward squarely with the top one curling upwards and that the tongue flattens out of sight in the *ah* sound. In saying 'round' take it slowly, beginning with the two vowel sounds, then combining into the full word: *rah-oo-rahoond*; it is good to get the *oo* position of the lips before you begin the word so that they are in readiness when the jaw drops for the *ah*.

When your students have done plenty of work with *ah*, *oo* and *ou* sounds they can go on with more varied exercises.

Intoning, for instance. Simply repeat a poem or read a passage on a single musical note – as a priest does in a church service. Run smoothly on without any break, the single note gives more carrying power than ordinary speaking and one has a stronger feeling of the voice being projected forward. It helps, in practice, if you begin by humming the note before forming the first word.

Follow the intoning exercises – which of course can be done on varying notes – by the complete contrast of inflexion practice. For this, swoop and throw the voice about with the utmost abandon and exaggeration, going up and down on single words and phrases. Attempt the most fantastic, dramatic burlesque, with no regard to the real sense of what you read.

Incidentally, for reading practice, use any anthology of verse, Gilbert and Sullivan, Shaw, Clemence Dane, Shakespeare. Much useful stuff can be found in *Punch*. Particularly good dialogue is in Shaw's *Man of Destiny* and *Arms and the Man*.

It is generally effective to lift the voice for key words and drop it at sentence ends. Breath failure often causes a sentence to die away towards its close and so makes the raising of the voice seem desirable, whereas what is really needed is to sustain power by having a reserve of breath whatever inflexion or pitch the sentence may have. Be particularly careful in reading verse to get end words strong.

See that the *R* is strong between vowels – *spirit*. In such words as *little* push the tongue hard forward, and say the *L* with vigour. Note that the *Y* ending of such words as *pretty*, *city*, is not really an *ee* sound but should be spoken with a dropping of the lower jaw.

Here are a few particular exercises, which can be repeated many times, with exaggerated emphasis, and special slowness, for the special vowel sounds.

Oo – Clear and cool, clear and cool, through laughing shadow and dreaming pool. – There was a young airman named Scroop, who would keep on looping the loop.

Ah – The cart is passing under the arch, of lacing boughs

of fir and larch; Harsh is the call of the night-jar's laugh and the barn is lit by the sparks from the hearth.

Ou – Drifting slowly round and round, sinking deep into the ground.

Er – What, haven't you heard of Edward the Third? Don't be so absurd, of course you have heard of Edward the Third.

Intoning practice. – Hum a note using the consonant, and without breaking open out into the vowel sounds: m-oo; m-ay (with jaw going down); m-ee (jaw down). For this next exercise be sure to stand – inhale; pull in the abdomen, and intone: one, two, three, four.

Oh – Monks of Rome from their home, where the blue seas break in foam. – Oh no man knows through what wild centuries roves back the rose.

Ee – The frost is here, and fuel is dear, and woods are sere and fires burn clear. – Each new year it would appear, he can see the highway clear.

Air – She hath no handmaid fair, to draw her curled gold hair, through rings of gold that bear her whole hair's weight. – There was a young student of Clare, who said, 'I am somewhere – but where? Though I fancy I am on the banks of the Cam, there's nothing to prove I am there.'

General Exercise. – Now we must rush, through snow and slush. – The monks and nuns all live on buns. – I foretold the result would be ceaseless tumult. – Oh hark, oh hear, how thin and clear, the horns of Elfland faintly blowing. – The apples are ripe, and ready to fall, and Robin and Reuben shall gather them all.

SPEAKING IN PUBLIC

It is good to get your members to tackle public speaking whenever they have the opportunity. But keep clearly in mind the fact that this is an entirely different matter. Voice production is the mechanics of speaking; public speaking involves the clear and audible transmission of what you have to say, it deals with what you have to transmit and how to make the content effective and memorable.

So let your students get on their feet as frequently as possible, for just a moment or two, and then have a frank and general criticism between yourselves.

Here are a few hints: Stand upright, but in easy, relaxed position. Don't begin speaking too soon. Glance round at your audience to make sure that they are attentive and waiting expectantly for you to begin. Have your opening sentence planned in advance, so that something fresh or forceful about it immediately attracts – don't just 'begin talking'. Don't stay immobile; turn occasionally so that all sections of the listeners in turn feel that you are addressing them. This impression is helped if, instead of looking directly into the eyes of individuals, your glance goes over their heads – this incidentally will help you to 'talk to the back row', enabling your voice to travel more effectively. Don't be afraid of using notes, if you must, or of letting the audience see them – better that than frequently stooping to get your bearings from a paper lying on the table. But don't read. What you have to say should be reduced to such simple planning that merely a few 'headlines' remind you of the progressive stages of your message. And when you have finished – stop! Notice how many speakers just can't manage to do this.

TAKING CHURCH SERVICES

Especially in the 'Free Churches' young people are often helped and interested by accompanying an adult who is 'going preaching'. But groups of teenagers can just as well take complete services by themselves, with or without adult aid. A cycling group, a party of hikers, a carload, a number travelling by bus, can arrive at the service place – indoors or outdoors and carry the thing through with fervour and sincerity.

Circumstances and setting will naturally determine the general pattern, but if you have an inexperienced group it may be well to plan as follows:

Discuss with them the general aim of worship – to become conscious of the presence of God, to be receptive to his guidance, to seek understanding of the Way of Jesus. Within this sort of scheme what are the functions of music, hymns, prayers, readings, silences, talk? Don't take for granted that the familiar forms of church service are ideal. Let your teenagers hammer out for themselves what they think to be the best combination of parts which will result in the desired total effect. Then apportion what each can do: music – what instrument; hymns – are words or tunes more important, and can both be good; prayers – extempore or read, addressed to God or Jesus, responsive or not; silences – have the Quakers something to teach, and how long can silence be borne anyhow; readings – should these be only from the Bible; solos – is there any place for these; talk – should one person give a full address or several speak for just a minute or two?

From such considerations your teenagers will formulate

their ideal service and you may justifiably hope that it will be helpful to all who join in it.

It should be hardly necessary to say that the ideal preparation for 'taking services' in the foregoing fashion is through the routine sharing and training of a healthy Youth Club's 'epilogues' or 'orisons'.

DEBATING

Debating is an excellent way of getting young people on their feet. It should be a continuing part of the club's activities.

In these days, because of modern publicity and mass media techniques, it is perhaps less easy than ever before for people to develop and hold individual opinions. So it is especially desirable that debates should be encouraged among young people. Debating helps the boy or girl to see various points of view and to express personal convictions.

But a debate, if it is to yield most benefit, should be properly conducted irrespective of whether the subject be 'That sweets be taxed' or 'That the European nations become a single Federation without delay'. The rules of debate, insofar as they apply to the usual club occasion, are simple enough:

At the outset the Chairman announces the *motion* or *resolution* which is to be discussed – it might be 'That parents are nearly always right'. The Proposer of the motion then rises and makes his opening speech, having been called on by the Chairman. The Proposer, and every later speaker, must 'address the Chair' – later speakers can easily fall into the way of speaking direct to other members, which usually results in noisy arguments and squabbles. A firm Chairman will insist that this does not occur and that all remarks are addressed primarily to him.

Supposing the Proposer is allowed three minutes; he is followed by the first speaker for the opposition, who should be allowed a similar three minutes. Next the Chairman calls on the Seconder of the motion – permitting him two minutes, and after him the second opposition speaker takes two minutes.

When these four principal speakers have had their turns the Chairman declares that the meeting is open for discussion – and anyone, other than the original four, is allowed a turn, perhaps lasting one minute. A would-be speaker must rise, so that he 'catches the Chairman's eye'. The Chairman must call on the person by name before he is allowed to speak and it is usually the one the Chairman sees first who is called, though he may use his discretion in making the debate more interesting by calling alternately, as far as he is able, on supporters and opposers of the motion. This is the period during which he must be especially careful to prevent wrangles and interruptions getting out of hand. A speaker may address the meeting only once, but when general discussion is concluded the chief opponent is given two more minutes, and the debate concludes with a final two-minute speech by the Proposer.

Then the Chairman 'puts the question'. He would probably say: 'The motion is, that parents are nearly always right. Will those who are in favour please vote by holding up one hand.' He counts the number of hands, and goes on: 'Will those who are against please show in a similar manner.' He counts again – Secretary can aid him in counting if desired – and concludes: 'The motion is carried' or 'the motion is lost' according as the votes have determined.

A POETRY GROUP

It may seem ambitious, it may seem nonsensical – but it may meet with surprising success. Are there any members of your club who would like to get together to read poetry? If any have done it before they will almost certainly be keen; if none have tried some persuasion may be necessary. A good plan is to ensure that for a week or two in advance several who are to take active part will be getting ready. For this they will need collections of poems from which to choose those they wish to read. They may already have their own books, or you can borrow anthologies from friends or the public library and lend these.

When the night comes, sit in a quiet corner or room in informal comfort, and let each person in turn read a poem that he or she likes – a comment on it before or after will be helpful. Readings should be short, and the genuine choices of the people concerned. Don't have any highbrow nonsense about the group – there is room for unintelligible modern stuff and equally for simple old ballads, and all the styles between.

Maybe after a few weeks some of your members may like to have a go at writing their own verse, and trying it out on the rest of you.

BALLET

Ballet might be an attractive new activity for your senior girls. Why not see if you can contact an instructress, through the local youth organisations, or direct application to a school of dancing. Given a capable attractive teacher, your girls may become really keen.

Don't have too much publicity at the outset, and let the girls start off behind locked doors. There will be plenty of aching muscles from the early limbering exercises and tentative first steps, and a few fainthearted may drop out. But those who remain will soon be abandoning jeans and shorts and attempts in socks or bare feet for real ballet shoes and tunics.

Of course they will go to see any available ballets, and equally will want to put on some sort of item at the next club entertainment.

PHOTOGRAPHER AT LARGE

If you know a competent photographer sufficiently friendly and imaginative to spend a few evenings in your club he may produce some very interesting pictures. Don't necessarily plan anything in advance but just turn him loose among the various club activities, looking for pictures. He may snap a chess game, an argument, eager faces at the canteen counter, a jive session, a cluster at the notice board, drama rehearsal. In short, genuine pictures of club life, each telling a story. How you pay; whether you sell; the way in which you display – all such things will give later points of interest.

SKETCHING

This, ideally, should be preceded by some guidance or instruction, but if this cannot be arranged you can still go ahead. Let everyone take a 'sketch-book', then all go together to some pre-arranged spot where there is a good 'subject'. It may be a church, cottage, bridge, hill, creek, cluster of trees. The important and very practical detail is that all your club members shall be able to settle down comfortably and do their sketching, without feeling conspicuous or overlooked. Allow as much time as you can. When you get back to the club the signed sketches may be displayed for general study.

CLIMBING DO'S AND DONT'S

Here is a code of rules for climbers put out by the British Mountaineering Council. **1.** Plan, with maps. Ask experienced people to help you; **2.** Don't try too much too soon. Move gradually to bigger things; **3.** Go with others and keep together always. Until experienced don't take charge of others, then take only ten or less; **4.** Equip against the worst. Be well shod, have warm clothing and a waterproof cover, spare clothes and food for all, map, whistle, torch and compass; **5.** Give yourself ample time, and more as a reserve. Move steadily. Don't hurry and don't waste time; **6.** Don't throw down or dislodge rocks or stones. Know and observe the Country Code; **7.** Eye the weather, it can change completely in a few hours. Don't go on recklessly if it turns bad. Don't be afraid to come down; **8.** Don't do rock, snow, or ice climbing, without an experienced leader; **9.** If lost, don't panic or rush down. Keep together and *deliberately* work out your position and your best way down; **10.** Leave word behind you of your route and when you expect to be back. If you can't arrive at a point where friends expect you, 'phone them or tell the police. (Do this to save needless search.)

SPELEOLOGY, OR CAVE EXPLORATION

Providing you live in a suitable district, the exploring of caves, and pot-holing, can be a fascinating club activity. It must be done, of course, under expert guidance. It can begin with a systematic study of the various types of rocks, their formations and encrustations. It can include courses of training in an Outward Bound School or courses run by Education Authorities. And it can be tied up with the Duke of Edinburgh's Award Scheme.

When the technique of cave exploration has become fairly familiar there can be training in methods of escape from awkward situations and ways of rescuing other persons in trouble. Helping an injured person along fissures, over ravines, along tricky passages, and through narrow openings – all such things can be involved. But first get some competent person to come to the club and give a general introductory talk.

ADVENTURE PLANNING

Adventurous projects which test the initiative, self-discipline and toughness of boys are excellent, and enjoyable. But to devise them within the framework of a club programme is not easy, for available time and the type of locality have so much bearing on what is practicable.

Perhaps the best plan is to let your dependable teenage boys themselves evolve the adventure they desire, and then tackle it singly or in pairs. Their age and previous experience will help them to set the standards of achievement – how many miles should they walk in a day, for example. The ingredients of the adventure can be most varied, and combined to taste: accomplishing a walk or climb within a given time; camping out in unfavourable conditions; being dropped into the middle of an unknown moor with the necessity of finding the way back by compass; travelling only by night and lying concealed through the day; sharing in 'work schemes' to serve the community or a particular unfortunate individual. You may discuss whether hitch-hiking should be permissible and how far proffered help should be accepted. Can money be earned en route? Can the adventure include some test of the ability to make courteous friendly approaches to strangers in order perhaps to gain written attestation that places have been reached or time-tables adhered to?

In short, for the club members keen on adventure, the preliminary planning of it will be almost as fascinating as the thing itself.

JUMPING

Jumping can be a useful outdoor or indoor club activity. Woodworker members will not have much difficulty in making the jumping stand. Then plan a brisk half-hour, with as many as possible taking part. Indoors, it must be 'standing jumps', of course.

In the simplest form of standing jump the jumper stands squarely facing the bar, with feet slightly apart. He raises his hands above the head, arms straight. Then the arms swing loosely downward and backward and the trunk bends forward, to allow the weight to go on to the front of the feet, with knees bending for the jump. The arms swing upward with fullest vigour, and a spring is made from the balls of the feet, the knees first straightening as they thrust the body upward, then drawing up quickly so that the feet may clear the bar. Practice will show how far from the jumping stand the person needs to be in order to be at maximum height of flight at the precise instant when he is over the bar. In landing, evenly on both feet, the knees must yield to reduce shock.

A club team should stand in single file for jumping practice, each stepping up smartly at the command word; making his jump; running round to the rear of the line. Start very low, so that everyone may have plenty of chances as the bar is gradually raised, and emphasise style and technique rather than height achievement.

When this plain jump is mastered a few extra inches may be gained by the rather more difficult scissors style. For this you stand sideways to the bar. If your jumping leg is the left your right side will be about 1½ ft from the bar, with feet slightly apart. The arms are raised and swung down and back, while a full breath is taken; the head will have turned to look at the bar; the trunk bends forward and the knees too bend. Without pause, the reverse movement follows, the whole body straightening as the arms swing vigorously upward. As the body rises vertically the right, near leg is swung upwards and over the bar, stretching straight to the front as it passes across. The left leg hangs down limply until its fellow is over, when it too is brought quickly forward and over. You land on the right foot, the left touching the floor a moment later, and the arms being still well raised. Style and neatness are of greatest importance in this scissors jumping, and they can only be acquired with practice at a low bar. Give a special heed to the vigorous up-swing of the arms and the free fling of the leg from the hip. A shock-absorbing landing is equally important.

Round about 3 ft is a good height for young teenagers.

CANOEING

Canoeing holidays are becoming increasingly popular, for they are usually fairly inexpensive, and have the extra advantage of being adventurous and off the beaten track. Your club members may have built their own canoes, in which case they probably know all about local opportunities and conditions. Otherwise, information on hiring canoes, routes, planned parties, can be readily obtained from hiring firms on your nearest stretch of water, or through the normal channels of local youth advisory bodies and education authorities.

A pre-requisite for a canoeing holiday is ability to swim at least 50 yards. Some knowledge of how to use a paddle is also desirable – and surprisingly rare among the many who sit in water craft and clutch paddles. Unless you have a two-ended paddle you should dip your blade and work on one side only of your canoe – not splashing wildly first on one side then the other. But to propel smoothly and strongly from the one side means that the tendency of the front of your craft to veer round from the force of each stroke must be counteracted. The whole art of paddling basically consists in flattening and pressing the blade outwards at the end of a backward stroke, thus keeping your canoe on its straight forward course.

In the ideal canoeing holiday there should be camping ashore each evening, with meals prepared by agreed members of the party – if several canoes are travelling together

– or by friends who chance to be convenient at the stopping point.

If you are on a river be sure to make full enquiries about the advantages of starting upstream or downstream, and the relative times needed with the current and against it. A holiday can be spoiled if one is battling exhaustingly upstream in the last day or two, trying to overtake a hindered timetable.

Youth hostelling may, of course, come into your plans, especially if you desire to canoe abroad, for continental hostels are often conveniently placed for this very purpose.

CROSS-COUNTRY RUNNING

This can become a popular speciality with boys. It may be an idea to start off in the autumn, and work towards a club championship, or inter-club contest, in the spring.

For regular practice it is good to have a home course of three or four miles, which can be frequently used in order that methods of dealing with such obstacles as a gate, a ditch, a hedge, a railing, a wall, can be developed. Each person evolves his own technique and style. Going over the same course frequently also gives runners the chance of comparing their methods with those of others and learning their own capabilities – just how many seconds are required for each type of obstacle; where to sprint; where to reduce speed, and so on. Just how to tackle a hill is also important – it is not usually wise to go up at too fast a pace, but it is often equally a mistake to slow to a walk and so lose the rhythm of running.

Tactics too – an opponent whose breathing is laboured and irregular is clearly weakening, and a sprint at that critical time may put him out of the running. A hard lesson to learn is how much or little to be influenced by an opponent – he may pull you on at a speed just above what is comfortable for you, and so much sap your strength that you have no reserve for the end of the race.

A team, for a cross-country race, should consist of a minimum of three boys, and the first three home in each team should count for scoring, according to their positions and points in the overall placings – the first boy being marked 1 point, the next 2, and so on. Thus that team wins which has, from its own first three home, the lowest number of points.

There are two particular advantages of this type of running – spiked shoes are the only special equipment, and the running is under such conditions that spectators and applause hardly come into it. The keenness of the runner is the prime motive for participation.

Oddments

The section title explains itself – here are practical items and ideas which do not so readily fit into earlier classifications.

BEGIN EARLY

What would seem to be an almost general condition in organized work among teenagers is that, usually, the 'club with a programme' is comparatively small, while the really large club rarely has any 'programme' in which all members participate. The 'open club' is often of this latter type, and teenagers with free time will swarm to it. Most of them will be earning, and so will have plenty of money.

Youngsters at Grammar School or Training College will have neither the leisure nor the money to enable them to fit in well. So those who do attend will probably spend most of their time with records, and maybe table-tennis. The keen leader is apt to be discouraged by the depressing picture of stolid indifference to any sort of wider interest or achievement, and with the feeling that nothing is being accomplished beyond 'keeping them off the street'. But the value of this should not be underrated. Companionship and association are what these young people most want, and need, and 'a place to go' is worth a lot. Perhaps, after a time, growing monotony and boredom may incite them to venture into some sort of 'programme features'!

But the real lesson of all this is that a taste for doing things that are worthwhile and mind-broadening must be developed early. Try therefore to have clubs for younger folk linked with your Youth Club. It is among the under 15's that the key work needs to be done. Catch them in Junior and Intermediate clubs, while the added stimulus of day school surrounds them, and you can make them see what a variety of fun and enjoyable self-expression can be had in a club programme. If for several years at this young age they learn what a real club can be, and how much its planning can depend on them, then they will carry over their experience into the Youth Club and insist that this has the same wide scope.

BREAKING DOWN DIVISIONS

A UNESCO report suggests that there is danger of youth being split into three clear groupings: 1. Those who are achieving all for which they had hoped, by attaining the fullest education in college and university, and so are clearly marked out to be the successful people of the future; 2. The disappointed ones, who had hoped to achieve but have failed and who can so easily become embittered and soured by their frustrations and poor showing; 3. Those without talents and ambitions, who expected little from life and are content to be always directed and controlled by others.

If these groupings should be extended and hardened they could result in a more cruel and rigid caste society than the past has ever known. The right sort of youth club can do a great deal in preventing such calamity, by showing both in principle and in practice how full and friendly life can be when service rather than self is its motive, as well as in giving the frustrated ones opportunities to prove their worth in ways which are worth-while and at the same time congenial to them.

OUT OF THE SHELL

So many young people remain 'in their shell'; they are shy, inhibited, nervous; what they need is to release their inner personality, to relax into natural self-expression, to realise themselves. Is it possible in your club programme to devise features, suited to your particular requirement, which will helpfully 'bring out' the shackled personalities? Here are suggestions which can form the basis of a series of planned evenings. Groups should not be too large – no more than ten, for example, can well take part in a talking session.

Hosts and Hostesses. On any formal or semi-formal occasion let a young host and hostess be responsible for receiving and welcoming guests; introducing them to each other appropriately – 'Jane, this is Hazel who, like you, is very keen on cycling'; watching that no one remains lonely; announcing whatever is going to happen, and generally having charge of the evening.

At Home. This can be something fairly elaborate, or merely the refreshment interval in a club evening. The point is that there shall be opportunity to hold a cup of tea or coffee, together with cake or biscuit, and to talk with friends – whilst some move about courteously supplying the needs of the seated ones, from tray or trolley. It is no easy matter for the inexperienced to avoid dropping crumbs or spilling from a cup, and only practice will give the relaxed ease which all would like to achieve.

For a more elaborate version of this get some capable friendly person to arrange an At Home at her house, sending an invitation to each member, and carrying the whole thing through just as it would be done with adults.

Miming and Play-reading. Play-reading is an excellent way of getting young people to 'loosen up'. Sets of books can easily be borrowed from a local library or education authority. A one-act play with casting suitable for your available members can be got going without previous preparation. Hand out the copies; give a quick outline of the play; let each have a few minutes to glance through – then off you go. Urge your folk to forget themselves and to live the characters.

Miming is perhaps more useful still in breaking down stiffness and reserve. Let your group sit about comfortably, and then allow each in turn to mime some emotion or situation, using facial expression, attitude, arms, to the full. Grief, joy, dread, anticipation, relief, mistrust – all such things offer plenty of scope.

Conversation. There can be two distinct aims in this. First, to develop stimulating 'table talk' or social conversation; second, to know how to put the shy person at ease and to see that he or she does not remain outside and neglected.

For this latter choose one of your group to be 'brought out', and let the others begin and sustain conversation originating from his particular interests, in which he thus easily shares. 'To be interested in the other person rather than yourself' might be the slogan for the rest.

To get intelligent, interesting talk, with all sharing, agree beforehand that several members shall in turn introduce topics to which all contribute as they may.

Dance Etiquette. Merely to walk across an empty floor in sight of all can be an acute ordeal. A dance gives opportunity for your boy to walk over and request the next dance. At the conclusion he must not abruptly desert his partner, but walk back with her to her place, with polite thanks, before returning to his own seat. All this sort of thing is of much value if the occasion is treated seriously in an effort to do the right thing well, but with natural poise and ease.

Dress. Teenagers are fortunately very dress conscious and always appreciate advice from competent folk who have their esteem. So get an occasional talk on 'what to wear and how', and see that formal occasions arise on which the appropriate clothes are insisted on.

GIRLS — BOYS — PROGRAMMES

In the ordinary mixed club there is often a marked difference in the attitudes of boys and girls towards activities. For instance boys will happily spend a whole evening at table-tennis or billiards, almost oblivious of the girls who stand around. The girls may occasionally have a game but clearly they are not very keen. On the other hand the girls can cheerfully occupy an evening dancing, and listening to records in between, if boys can be persuaded to stay around and join in occasionally.

A broad generalization can be adduced from this – boys see an activity as an end in itself, and see the association with girls, during its practice, as a pleasant but inessential thing. Girls see association and relationships with others, especially with boys, as the primary thing, and the activity is merely the means of getting this friendly contact. Once this principle is realised it can help considerably in arousing general interest in programme planning.

You want the club to do a hike? The boys will be attracted by the achievement and interest value – the distance, the difficulties, the points of interest; the appeal to the girls will be much more as to the manner in which the hike is made – the chances of pairing off, sharing with friends, enjoying group contacts.

So in introducing any scheme, try to get a separate strong angle of appeal both to your boys and your girls.

AN EASTER IDEA

One small town youth club, at Easter, got permission from its local council to erect a 9 ft. cross on the roadside at each entrance to the town. Motorists and other folk entering throughout Holy Week were made to think by the stark, unexpected symbol.

Is this an idea for your club? Next Easter may seem a long way off, but a big scheme needs long planning.

THE PROBATION OFFICER

Do you keep contact with your local Probation officials? A Youth Club can be helpful in settling a maladjusted boy or girl – so often understanding friendship and normal healthy surroundings are the things most needed. Let it be known to your Probation Officer that you are prepared to have a go when he has a particular individual who, he thinks, might be helped by the services you can offer. There may chance to be a Remand Home in the district whose young people might benefit a lot by an occasional meeting – perhaps for a Games Evening – with your own club members. Anyhow, look into the possibilities.

PARENTS' MEETING

Teenagers spend little time at home, and the gap between them and their parents is often very wide. Have you tried a joint session of teenagers and parents? Frank and revealing discussion may be possible at such a Parents' Meeting, where, with a larger but still friendly audience, talk may be freer. But guide the talk carefully, with such topics as: Why is home dull? Our different outlooks and interests; Spare time; What makes a happy family? When is one grown up? How much freedom is good? Bringing friends home.

PUSH FOR PUBLICITY

You want to advertise your club? Why not get some sort of truck, or a collection of old prams, and push it or them perhaps ten miles – relays of members may take it in turn. Posters, fancy dress, tableaux – anything of this sort can be helpful, their aim being to attract attention and to make folk aware that your club is responsible for all this – with the implication that it is a club full of energy and fresh ideas. Incidentally, if fêtes or carnival competitions occur in your district there may be opportunity for your club to make its own entry along these same lines.

WAYS OF HELPING

Most Youth groups nowadays are eager to do their share in the constant 'war against want' and so on. But how to help, and how to raise money? Here are suggestions: collecting gifts which can later be sold in shops or by other means; collecting good warm clothing; putting on film shows – films and filmstrips can readily be obtained; displays of photographs and posters; exhibition to bring home to people the grievous needs in so many parts of the world; special collections; a mile of pennies – or part of a mile, it works out at 2s. 6d. a yard; knitting blankets and making baby clothes; concerts and entertainments; famine meals – charging ordinary price but giving only 'famine ration', perhaps water and cooked rice; barbecue; sports day; fishing competition; self denial week; Bring and Buy Sale – each bring something, and each buy something; holiday work – proceeds being donated; silver paper collecting; windfall apples collecting and selling; garden party or fête; jumble sale; market stall; dances; book sale.

CONTACTS

The club leader, concentrating all the time on immediate problems, often feels he is working in isolation. That, of course, is not at all true. Though it may seem that no-one really cares whether you succeed or fail with your young folk, and even that no-one else is trying to do anything about them, yet a more relaxed consideration will show what a lot of adults really share your concern. Parents, for example – perhaps you don't often meet them or hear their views, but you can be sure that most of them genuinely appreciate whatever is being done for their children's welfare. Sincere Church folk too will be wishing you well, though they may have little chance, or ability, to tell you so. Then the day-school teachers, who spend much more time with teenagers than you are able to do – their knowledge and interest, if you are able to check on it, would often surprise you. The Youth Employment Officer – do you know anything of him or her – is often vitally concerned about your individual club members at the most crucial times of their lives. And the local Youth Organiser – do you take full advantage of whatever help and advice he can provide? Besides all these there are a surprising number of adults around you who, though feeling unable to give any practical help themselves, yet warmly approve the work of any who try to guide youth.

Make contact with all such co-workers and sympathisers whenever you can. Almost certainly they will be just as pleased to know you as you will be to know them. In the human sense, it is most certainly true, for those who love and serve young people, that 'we are not alone'; on the spiritual plane it is more true still.

NEW MEMBER RECEPTION

Receiving new members should always be an important and formal business. It is good to let the club committee work out its own details, so that the ceremony really is individual and traditional. The items which go towards the full ceremony may include: *Introduction* – the new member is introduced by name and perhaps reported as 'having satisfactorily completed the probationary period with the approval of the Committee'; *Welcome* – a handshake from the leader or someone else; *Loyalties or Duties* – the new member makes some response to, perhaps, 'will you remember always your duty to this Club; Your duty to others; Your duty to God'; *Creed or Affirmation* – which might be as follows:

> *This is our Club,*
> *Let peace dwell here,*
> *Let the room be full of contentment.*
> *Let love abide here –*
> *Love of one another,*
> *Love of mankind,*
> *Love of life itself,*
> *And love of God.*
> *Let us remember*
> *That as many hands build a house,*
> *So many hearts make a club.*

Prayer – it could be:

> *Lord Jesus, faithful Comrade,*
> *We meet to learn of Thee;*
> *Teach us, as we before Thee stand,*

To play and labour hand in hand,
And faithful comrades be. Amen.

Club Anthem or Hymn – if you have one.

SUMMER REVIEW

Early summer is a good time for the whole club to review its finances. Presumably annual payments and large items are settled at the end or beginning of each year. In June or July you can get a general picture of how the money has come in and gone out over the twelve months, and as summer is usually considered the end of the club's seasonal year, you may consider whether the balance in hand justifies some sort of 'splash', like an outing, or whether some long desired bit of equipment cannot be purchased to start off the approaching Autumn session.

It may be opportune also to consider subscriptions, arrears, canteen profits, and so on, against the whole picture of club finances.

MAKE A BANNER

Have you a banner in your club? Why not make one – it is so useful on special occasions, especially out of doors.

The first thing is to buy the material, perhaps $1\frac{1}{2}$ yds of 36 ins bunting. Various colours are available; gold can make an excellent background with blue lettering. The amount of blue bunting needed will depend on how much lettering you desire.

Cut out the letters and sew them on to the background, with blanket stitching.

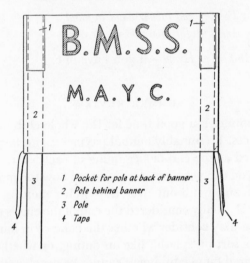

1 Pocket for pole at back of banner
2 Pole behind banner
3 Pole
4 Tape

A slot or hem, about 1½ ins wide and 6 ins deep is needed at each top corner – into these the poles fit. Tape a yard or so long should be sewn to the bottom corners, by which the banner is held taut. For poles, the most serviceable and cheap solution is chimney-sweep rods. These are each 3 ft long and screw into each other, so that three rods make a 9 ft pole, and with this useful height the poles can stand on the ground and folk can walk underneath the banner if desired. For indoor use at a club meeting poles can be 6 ft, and leaned against the wall. For packing and transport the rods, with banner round them, can go into a narrow bag only a yard long.

PROGRAMME ON THE NOTICE-BOARD

Probably the best way of planning your programme is in four sessions or terms or seasons: Autumn to Christmas;

Christmas to Easter; Easter to end of June; July to October. The 13-week stretch should be planned in advance so that all members are informed and preparations can be made for as many weeks ahead as may be necessary. Get your programme prominently displayed on the notice-board, and as originally and decoratively produced as you can make it. If it is to attract attention and stimulate comment it must be fresh in wording, even humorous or flippant, though at the same time clear and factual. To hold the balance, in programme features, between items produced by members and those made possible by external help, is an essential and not an easy matter. If you have visiting speakers or demonstrators it is good to plan them at regular intervals, possibly the first week in each month, so that their dates are easily remembered. Be sure to keep the club committee prominent, accepting responsibility and being always available and accountable to their fellow members.

Your programme for the first quarter of the year might be something like this (though, of course, typed or laid out decoratively on a large sheet): *January 12th* – Quiz Team Contests (What do you know!); *19th* – Western evening (only those properly dressed admitted. Guns need not be parked); *26th* – Debate (no speech to exceed 90 minutes); *February 2nd* – Distinguished Visitor; *9th* – Club Supper and Entertainment (bring knife, fork, indigestion tablet); *16th* – Club Leader's Mystery Evening (Oh dear!); *23rd* – Première of new Club Song, by assistant Club Leader (Oh no!); *March 2nd* – Distinguished Visitor; *9th* – Old friends as Club Guests (Toujours la politesse); *16th* – Indoor Sports (all queries to Club Secretary who knows all the answers);

23rd – Impromptu Speeches (only one at a time); *30th* – Beetle Drive (those who bring pencils deserve to win); *April 6th* – Distinguished Visitor; *13th* – Blank; *20th* – Good Friday. (Still more brainwaves to come. Trust your Committee. If no brainwaves, sack your Committee!) *Your Committee:* Virginia H. (Secretary), Martin S. (Treasurer), Susan O., Barry N., Sandra J., Roger P.

VICE-PRESIDENTS, AND OTHERS

Many clubs have Vice-Presidents or similar groups of adults, who take a personal interest in club affairs. Maybe they provide an annual supper or tea, and themselves attend. When such an occasion occurs be sure that they are made very welcome. Metaphorically, or actually, put out the red carpet for them. One excellent plan is to fill the notice-board with greetings and special features. You might, for example, have one huge poster: 'Hurrah for our Vice-Presidents'. Or decorative rhymed couplets, like the following, might adorn the board: For the Party and the Teas, Thanks a lot, you kind V-Ps; Three cheers, if you please, For our honoured V-Ps.

Anyhow, make your special visitors very conscious of the fact that you are proud and glad to have them with you.

REFRESHMENT TICKETS

When you have a Social or Concert with a refreshment interval it is often time-wasting and troublesome if each person has to pay on the spot. A useful alternative method is to have 'Refreshment Tickets' which can be bought at the door or before the evening's programme begins. All you have to do is to get a few rolls of cloakroom tickets of different prices, perhaps 3d., 6d., 9d., the holders of which would then be entitled to (maybe): a cup of tea, tea and cake, tea with cake and sandwich.

The caterers will be helped by this method since they will have warning of how many tickets have been sold and what preparation they need to make.

REPORTING BACK

When a club member makes some special trip or excursion – to a museum, mountain, unfamiliar town, or almost any-where else – let him report on it to the club when he gets back, producing souvenirs or map or pictures to add to the interest. This is an easy way of getting folk to talk, but it should be done formally and properly.

CLUB FURNITURE

Most clubs have to meet in a hall or on premises which are not their own property but are hired or shared with other people. The extreme example is perhaps the classroom of a day-school, littered with desks and school equipment. In any such room it is difficult to get the feeling that 'this is our club', but the success or failure of the club will in con-siderable degree depend on how much this feeling is achieved. So it is good to consider the matter frankly with your club members.

What clearance can be effected by removing impedi-ments out of the way, and preferably out of sight? What marked change in appearance can you make to the whole room for the brief period of your occupation – have you hangings, banners, pictures, posters? Could you organize a colourful coffee bar or servery in one corner?

The entrance is important. It may be fairly easy to set off the tone and character of the club there, by a wide array of posters and notices. A large folding draught screen – cheap enough at a secondhand furniture store – can hold a lot of display stuff, especially if both sides are used. A clothes horse may be a substitute.

Set your members the task of transforming *the* room into *their* room, and you may be surprised how much can be done.

MEMBERS' COMMITTEE

Youthful committees like to meet, and to have a worthwhile agenda when they do meet. In addition to the routine items arising from the week to week working of the club, it is good occasionally to discuss more general matters. Here are suggestions:

1. Review membership attendance over last three months.

2. Consider whether there are any ways in which the inside of your premises could be improved, especially ways in which club members might assist.

3. Consider the outside of club premises and its surrounds. Would it be possible to make improvements by mending paths or by planting trees, shrubs, evergreens? Discuss with the responsible people the necessary purchases, and work, and could the club undertake it?

4. Are subscriptions being paid regularly – and are they adequate?

5. When a fellow club member is ill or in hospital arrange a rota, so that he or she receives a letter or card every day. Revise or renew your rota at each club meeting.

6. How are the club funds? What about a quick Jumble Sale? With every member really active; as much publicity as you can get; efficient and well organized collecting, you should get good results – and all within a week or two.

7. Organize a competition for a Club song or 'Anthem', allowing perhaps one week for competitors to plan and present their efforts, so that the resultant verses can be judged and sung afterwards. It is best to suggest the general style and pattern to be followed. You might have, for example, a Club Anthem, extolling your club and fitting *Auld Lang Syne*, or a ballad describing some club event and introducing personalities and happenings. (See *Music and Dancing* section, page 103.)

8. Do research, and report on 'Winter – or Summer– difficulties of the Club'.

9. Plan and rehearse carols. If you have a carol party in mind, you will need to think about collecting boxes, police permission to collect, instrumental accompaniment, copies of words, lighting, and so on. (See page 112.)

10. Review year's achievements, and failures.

11. Prepare a statement or programme outline to convince your members that the New Year is going to be the best ever.

NEIGHBOURLINESS

The sort of ideas listed here are such as may be commended, at the right moments, to club members, by conversation or by the notice-board, or by recommendation from the Members Committee. Fuller suggestions are in the *Continuing Interests* section, page 145).

1. A Self-Denial Week for some cause which really appeals to your members. The boys and girls may like to say in advance what they propose to do without – cinema, ices, and suchlike. They can take the thing very seriously, and still get a lot of fun from it.

2. Could you supply, or chop, any firewood for needy old people?

3. How can the club be of service if deep snow comes (see page 145).

4. Can any of your members help neighbours by taking dogs out for exercise?

5. Bring real information about a person needing assistance or friendliness, with practical suggestions as to how the Club could be of help.

6. Tidy up someone's garden for the winter, disposing of the rubbish.

7. Could some of the older members do baby-sitting – for a nominal fee, which might be handed in to some club or church or other needy fund.

8. Could the Club, having raised the necessary money, take a party of old people, or others, for a day's outing – or even provide them with a short holiday?

9. Which old people, locally, can be helped, and how? Could some of your members plant or weed gardens? Could some do housework? Could some help with making or repairing clothes? Could some even cut hair?

10. Produce out-of-the-ordinary club ideas for the New Year.

11. Falls can be dangerous to old people – so when there is ice about see if you can do errands for those who do not like to venture out.

12. Watch for white walking sticks. If you see a blind person hesitating at a kerb touch his arm and say, 'Can I cross the road with you?'

13. Often a person stands at a telephone kiosk or a postage-stamp machine in difficulty through having no change. It might be a good plan for you to be prepared if the request comes to you: 'Could you help me with change for sixpence?'

Index